POET

SOUTH LANCASHIRE

Edited by Simon Harwin

First published in Great Britain in 2003 by
YOUNG WRITERS
Remus House,
Coltsfoot Drive,
Peterborough, PE2 9JX
Telephone (01733) 890066

HB ISBN 0 75434 313 8
SB ISBN 0 75434 314 6

FOREWORD

This year, the Young Writers' The Write Stuff! competition proudly presents a showcase of the best poetic talent from over 40,000 up-and-coming writers nationwide.

Young Writers was established in 1991 and we are still successful, even in today's modern world, in promoting and encouraging the reading and writing of poetry.

The thought, effort, imagination and hard work put into each poem impressed us all, and once again, the task of selecting poems was a difficult one, but nevertheless, an enjoyable experience.

We hope you are as pleased as we are with the final selection and that you and your family continue to be entertained with *The Write Stuff! South Lancashire* for many years to come.

CONTENTS

Samantha Sheehan	83
Shane Jones	84
Joshua Glover	84
Elizabeth Gardener	85
Jennifer Blackburn	85
Louise Wood	86
Emma-Jane Leyland	86
Rachael Edwards	87
Rachel Ashurst	87
Hannah Hughes	88
Thomas Corsair	88
Laura Holcroft	89
Daniel Hull	89
Gabrielle Harrison	90
Thomas Foster	90
Simon Egerton	91
Jessica McKay	92
Kate Houghton	92
Rachel Barton	93
Briony McNelly	94
Sophie Oxenham	94
James Whyte	95
Jessica Woodward	95
Thomas Smith	96
Claire Harvey	96
Jemma McGuigan	97
Jake Almond	97
Liam Hall	98
David Cooper	98
Adam Jones	99
Sean Walsh	99
Michael Leonard	100
Jodie Garner	100
Laura Kavaney	101
Samantha Singleton	101
Katharine Christopher	102
Hayleigh Cross	102
Nicola Simpson	103

Rebecca Lyon	104
Daniel Podesta	104
Leah Roberts	105
Sophie Taylor	106
Todd Fishwick	106
Martin Egerton	107
Lewis North	108
Gemma Withington	108
Luke Pietraszko	109
Andrew Higgins	110
Tim Halliday	110
Zoe Jackson	111
Graeme Holden	112

St Gabriel's RC High School, Bury

Lauren Patton	112
Tom McMahon	113
Daryl Myers	113
Melanie Willan	114
Danielle Knight	114
Amy Hall	115
Samantha Bowker	115
Siobhán Murphy	116
Charlotte Miller	116
Rebecca Proctor	117
Alec Roughley	117
Daniel Cassidy	118
Faith Collinge	118
Michael Molloy	119
Grace Adams	119
Rebecca Roberts	120
James Raynard	120
Raisa Richardson	121
Amy Cosgrove	121
Daniel Horwood	122
Jonathan Mayall	122
Caroline Jane Dunne	123
Amber Keown	123

The Poems

MY FAMILY

We love our family very much,
But we can still hate or dislike
Someone at the same time.
Your mum gets your lunch ready
And she gets your uniform ironed.
Your dad rushes to work
Without getting his morning cup of tea.
When you feel sick, your family is there
To help you get better.
When you are upset they want to help you,
So the next time you feel like
Hitting or calling your family,
Just remember they love you.

Kirsty Louise Glicklich (12)
George Tomlinson School

HALLOWE'EN

The special day is coming,
This day is Hallowe'en
With goblins, evil spirits and grotesque things
I shouldn't have seen
Laughing while torturing things
With axes, stones and knives
Killing lots of children, teenagers, husbands and wives
Staying in their big dark caves,
Eating meat right off the bone
If you see them, run away,
Leave these things alone.

Chris Long
George Tomlinson School

THE MAN IN THE PICTURE

There's a picture at my nan's house,
She says it's magical, she got it years ago
A gift from her mum.

There's a man in the picture
Who just sits and stares,
Frozen in time, sat on his chair.

He smiles all day without a care,
Who wonders what he dreams
Or what he thinks.

He's real in his world but just a drawing in ours,
With a wink of the man's eye
He comes alive.

The man in the picture used to smile at me
But one day the man in the chair
Was no longer there.

Gillian Hart (12)
George Tomlinson School

THE GALAXY

The Galaxy is far and wide,
It's full of planets and shooting stars,
Nobody knows what lies out there,
Such emptiness is hard to bear.
When finally we discover,
Whatever is hiding out there,
We're maybe in a state of shock or despair.

Chantelle Clarke (12)
George Tomlinson School

UNTITLED

There was a mirror that showed you the truth.
It was the king. He used to laugh at all the poor people.

Till one day he gave it away.
The people threw it in the bin.
Whoever cracked the mirror would live forever.

The king hunted high and low for it
And a poor person cracked it.
His hands glowed up in the dark.

News travelled fast.
The king found him and the poor man took the crown.
All the poor man's family was happy as can be.

They were happy as Larry
Counting their money
Eating their honey.

Kathryn Snape (14)
George Tomlinson School

SEA LIFE

You would not think an octopus so small,
Is the worst animal of them all.
A lionfish with its poisonous spine,
That can give you a sting at any time.
Very long is a fully grown whale,
A sea horse holds on by its tail.
A hermit crab's shell is very weird,
A great white shark is greatly feared.
A stingray with its good camouflage
And a crab with mouth so large.

Daniel Lee Millington (12)
George Tomlinson School

CAMELOT

In a far away land,
O'er hills, across lakes,
Lies a magical kingdom
Called Camelot.

On the throne sits King Arthur,
Powerful and respected.
By his side sits Queen Guinevere,
Beautiful and loved.

At the round table sit
Bold knights in shining armour.
Sir Lancelot, Sir Galahad, Sir Percival
And many more.

In Avalon live the magic folk:
Wise Merlin, Arthur's friend and advisor
And Morgan, the Lady of the lake,
Who goes by many names.

Although these people and places
Are seen and heard no more
The legend of Camelot lives on
And will last forever more.

Marrissa Caitlin Feeney (12)
George Tomlinson School

FAERIES

Softly through the air they fly
Daintily tiptoeing on flower petals
Climbing without trouble, trees so high
Smelling each rose or daisy they see.

Making music with the help of birds' songs
Sipping gently, honeydew from tiny acorns
Dancing merrily, all night long, in a circle of toadstools
In pretty dresses made from spiders' silk and soft tree bark
Magically they disappear as dusk turns to dawn.

Emily Blakeway (12)
George Tomlinson School

SUNSET

I sat on the beach watching the sunset,
The most beautiful thing I have ever seen.
I was with the right man at the right time,
It was like I was living a dream.

The sunset is gorgeous in summer
And even in winter.
In fact it's gorgeous whenever
You go to see the sunset.

It does not matter where I am,
In Britain or abroad, in rain or shine.
It is just the fact I am watching the sunset,
With the right man at the right time.

It is better than the morning,
When the sun rises from the east.
I was lying on the beach at night,
Watching it set in the west.

I sat on the beach watching the sunset,
The most beautiful thing I have ever seen.
I was with the right man at the right time,
It was like I was living a dream.

Natalie Spinks (12)
George Tomlinson School

WAR

War is a time of hatred with others,
Even other people would lose their lovers.
War is a time of bomb shelters and planes,
Children would be evacuated on goodbye trains.
Tears, they were shed and hearts, they were broken,
When war was declared and Hitler had spoken.
The tanks were filled and guns were prepared,
When war was ready everyone was scared.
The Germans would come, ready to attack,
They would come with weapons and wouldn't look back.
The blackouts are gone and happiness will return,
The Germans have lost so now they will learn
That war is now over so away goes the pain,
Until Hitler declares war and evil strikes again.

Danielle Carss (12)
George Tomlinson School

THE GALAXY

The Galaxy is so far away
The sun, the moon and stars
When you look up at night
Don't you wonder where they are?
All those planets so far away
Those planets you will never see
No one has ever been neither you nor me
You might go up and see the moon
Some astronauts have been
But if you do go up there
You may never again be seen!

Georgina Birtwistle (12)
George Tomlinson School

MUSIC AROUND US

Music, music, music, it is all around us.
Rap, hip-hop, dance and trance
Big-up for the massive ravers.
1970, the birth of the buzzin' guitar
Pink Floyd, Deep Purple, Rainbow was all you heard in the Spar.
1980, hip-hop first came about,
Dr Dre, Snoop Dogg gave out a massive shout.
1990, pop was the new sensation,
S Club, Spice Girls sang with anticipation
And here is the new millennium,
I wonder what it will bring?
Whatever it is, it will surely start with a bing.

Kiefer Beckett (13)
George Tomlinson School

SPACE

Space is *humungous.*
Space is as black as coal.
Space holds many mysteries and secrets.
It goes on for miles and miles.
It may hold other lifeforms!
We may not be alone
In this huge wide universe,
But whatever the universe holds,
We have only really just started
To discover its many secrets,
But in a few centuries,
We may even be having holidays,
Up there, in space!

Liam O'Connor (12)
George Tomlinson School

THE OTHER NIGHT I HAD A DREAM . . .

My friend and I were in a horrible war
All those shocks and sudden deaths I've never known before

The air was cold and the sky was grey
Even though it was just a dream I'll never forget that day

Screams, shouts, cries all around
I was on my own, no friends could be found

I searched everywhere, frightened on my own
I thought about my friends, could they be all alone?

There was blood all around, planes in the sky
Suddenly I broke down and began to cry

Then I woke up in bed hysterically
A sigh of relief came over me, I smiled happily.

Jessica Lee (12)
George Tomlinson School

LIONS

Lions they are the king of the jungle,
They are the biggest of the cats,
They're fierce, they're strong, they're majestic,
They live together in a pride,
Their manes are magnificent,
Their claws are crafty
And they stalk their prey with stealth.

Jacob McDermott (12)
George Tomlinson School

ANIMALS OF THE WORLD!

This is about the animals across each land,
Some live in trees or even on the sand,
But wherever they are I will always see
How much the animals mean to me.

First there is the tiger, the silent of them all,
He runs and prowls and jogs a lot and maybe even crawls.

Next there is the barracuda who sails as fast as light.
He is very tough and won't go without a troubled fight!

Last there is the elephant that's as big as a house.
The tale is that it goes crazy over a mouse!

That's a list of my animals that are all quite rare,
So stop the poaching or I will get my friend the bear.

Conrad Greensmith (12)
George Tomlinson School

THE WEATHER

Autumn is here, summer has now gone.
It's started to get colder, so we put our woollies on.
The wind starts to blow, the rain begins to fall,
Out come the brollies, raincoats and all.
Winter will follow, things begin to freeze.
Snow starts to fall, covering all the trees.
Spring comes next, buds begin to show,
It's starting to get warmer, the farmers start to sow.
Summer is beginning, the flowers are in bloom,
We know that summer's here again, it's the end of June.

Nicola Fletcher (14)
George Tomlinson School

THE MONTHS

January brings new hope and dreams,
and people can work as teams.

February brings loveliness,
with lots of happiness.

March brings a slight breeze,
with lots of dancing trees.

April brings the Easter bunny,
and fills up children's tummies.

May brings the newborn,
awakened by the bright dawn.

June brings cooling showers,
which makes beautiful flowers.

July brings the children out to play,
on the street all day.

August brings out the hot sun,
and children have lots of fun.

September brings a new school year,
the new children have fear.

October brings Hallowe'en,
children dress up, play and scream.

November brings fireworks of red, blue and white
they all are so very bright.

December brings Christmas time,
all until the clock goes chime.

1 ... 2 ... 3 ... 4 ... 5 ... 6 ... 7
... 8 ... 9 ... 10 ... 11 ... 12 ... *chime!*

Ragen Burdett (12)
George Tomlinson School

OTTER

As I sat on the river bank
Watching the world go by,
I saw no movement in the water,
Then suddenly at the corner of my eye
I saw an otter swimming swiftly
To and fro through the water.

As I watched it swimming
Another one appeared.
They swam towards each other
And diving disappeared
Into the deep where
Fish swam away to hide.

I sat there watching and nothing happened
And then a nose appeared.
It moved towards the river bank
And raised its head and stared
And caught a glimpse of me.

It came closer and leant its head to one side.
It looked confused.
I think to see a creature like me,
So quiet and not hunting
It was a surprise.

The sun was going down,
I had to go in, so I decided
To watch it go for its last swim
And watch it disappear into the dark.

Lucy Rebecca Blakeway (12)
George Tomlinson School

MY CAT

I have a cat called Arnie,
He's good at catching mice,
He brings them back as presents
And leaves them at the door.

When my mum comes down in the morning
He scratches at the door,
Because he wants to be fed
And he doesn't like to be ignored.

Arnie will then come upstairs
And come into my room,
Miaowing his little head off
Just to wake me up.

Then he'll run downstairs again
And sit next to his cat bowl,
So we'll all come down and feed him
Which will make him big and fat.

After that he'll go outside
To sleep on the garage roof
Only so when you open the window
He can shoot inside miaowing
And curl up for a while.

He will go back out again
Running round catching mice and birds,
But if another cat came along
To try and eat his trophies
He would throw a fit there and then
And scare the poor thing away.

One day when we had a barbecue
He almost jumped on it,
But if he had succeeded he would have
Got a surprise!

Well this is my cat, Arnie, he really doesn't care
What you say about him.
I just hope he lives for a long time
With all his antics, and one day pass away,
But hopefully not for a while.

Beverley Heighway (12)
George Tomlinson School

HOLIDAYS

Holidays are cool,
Holidays are great!
I'm going on holiday
And I just can't wait!

We're going to a foreign place,
A place that's far away!
We are going for two weeks
Or we might just stay!"

Hot places, cold places,
They are all the same to me,
Lots of things to do,
Lots of things to see!

Whenever I'm on holiday,
I make some more new friends!
Which is why I'm usually sad,
To see my holiday end!

That's why I buy a keepsake,
A special little gift,
That reminds me of my holiday
And gives me a little lift!

Rebecca Heaton (12)
George Tomlinson School

THE WOES OF LIFE

The blackened clouds are forming
And now the rain must fall,
My care for this world is all but spent,
Just as my love has gone
And so once again I must find a new reason to live,
But where can such a goal be found?
In life itself of course,
Where everything is either true or not
And the difference is not always clear,
What a cruel world this is
And so as anything is possible,
Everything has a beginning
And everything must come to an end.
As it is said, nothing can or will last forever.
That's life.

Andrew Fletcher (14)
George Tomlinson School

HOLIDAYS

Holidays are fun, holidays are cool
You can spend lots of time in the swimming pool.
Holidays are great,
Especially with your best mates.
Holidays are about going abroad,
Holidays mean you shouldn't be bored.
Holidays are when you relax
And don't worry about your eye contacts.
Holidays are something you should enjoy.
Holidays are hanging out with the boys.

James Templeman (12)
George Tomlinson School

MONSTERS UNDER THE BED

Have you heard the noises?
Have you seen the glowing eyes?
Did you hear the soft roars
Echoing in the skies?
Was it little spiders
Or maybe it was a mouse?
Or maybe it was killer rats
Running around the house?
Or maybe it was none of these
That I've already said
You never know . . .
It could be . . .
Monsters under the bed.

Rebecca Brett-Edwards (12)
George Tomlinson School

THE WEEKEND

Weekend's here, going away
My dad said my mate can stay.
In the car - journey long
My mum liked to sing a song.
We arrived, it was dark
Sleeping in a caravan all night.
Eerie sounds from all around
Hurry morning, time's so slow.
Lots to do cycling around
Making friends from every town.
Time to go, Sunday night
Back to school, same old sights!

Robin Yorke (13)
George Tomlinson School

WINTER

Winter has arrived, the dying is done,
Another month to go then a new year will have begun.
Winter is cold, there is not much life to see,
But there is a lot of love and charity wherever you may be.

At Christmas time you will be very surprised,
With the mountains of presents right before your eyes.
They come in different sizes, some big some small,
But you never seem to take your eyes off them all.

Wintertime is a family time where everyone gets together,
You sing Christmas songs and drink wine
And wish it would last forever.
Now at last it's time to say goodbye to the year,
'Happy New Year,' let's go with a *cheer!*

Bethany Larkin (12)
George Tomlinson School

VISION

Vision is good,
Vision is swell,
But imagine if you were blind,
How horrible it would be,
Not to see the beautiful butterflies
Or the animals at the zoo,
Not to be able to see the glorious colours
Or the clouds in the sky,
Just think what it would be like,
Do not take your eyes
For *granted.*

Kimberley Mellor (12)
George Tomlinson School

POEMS

Poems are happy, poems are sad,
Poems are all things good and bad.

If you're sad and if you're down,
What you read might make you frown.

Sitting down reading a book
A little picture makes you look.

This might be your favourite poem,
Whether it's about Michael Owen,
Poems, they're so good!

Michael Tatlock (14)
George Tomlinson School

NIGHT TO DAY

Stars to the left,
Stars to the right,
They all shone bright
On that dark blue skied night.
Bright red sunrise against
A shimmering green-blue sea,
I love that midday sun on me.
Droplets of sea water spray over the rocks
Which faced a lighthouse, which
Searched the calm swaying ocean.

Michelle Higo (14)
George Tomlinson School

CREATURES OF THE NIGHT

When you go to bed at night
The world seems to fall into darkness
Nothing moves or speaks
And everywhere is silent and asleep

The only thing that seems to stay awake
At night is the wind
Continuously blowing against the trees
Leaves rustle and tremble
But take a closer look and you'll find that
Not everything is what it seems at night

For the night when it comes, is alive
Unimaginable creatures awaken
Things with pointy ears and wings come to life
Bringing with them the mysteries of the night

Faint forces and sounds of laughter are carried by the wind
Small figures drift through the midnight sky
And tiptoe along the deserted floor
Travelling further into the shadows

Then, when the day comes and sun rises
Everything that awoke during the night is now asleep
Invisible to the eyes of the now awakening world.

Alexandra Willkinson (12)
George Tomlinson School

LOVE

The many tears I have cried, will not bring you back,
Nor will what I feel.
I have wished so hard just to see you again,
Will this pain ever heal?

The love we shared was special,
The love we shared was true,
There is a hole in my heart and a gap in my mind,
All because I have lost you.

Words could never express
The emptiness that I feel.
I understand that you have gone,
But it still does not seem real.

Our love will last forever,
As will the memories in my heart.
Our silent bond will never be broken,
Till the day that I will part.

Then we will be together again,
United we will stand.
Always together, never apart,
Always hand in hand.

Sophie Wrigley (12)
Hope High School

THE SEED

Some time ago, I ate an apple
And in it was a seed.
I planted it in a garden tub
For every loving need.

Day by day, and week by week,
I watched it raise the earth.
I watched it grow a tiny leaf,
It was a tree's new birth.

Month by month it grew a stem
And over a foot in height.
To marvel over my apple plant,
Was truly a wonderful sight.

When winter came, it soon got cold,
I brought it into the warm.
To protect my apple plant from the frost,
The icy snow and storms.

My apple plant soon grew fruit,
Now it was a tree.
It always receives an annual visit,
From my family and me!

For now he stays high on a hill,
Where people can see and look
At the one lone tree high on the hill,
In the country by the Brooke.

Hayley Weibrecht (14)
Hope High School

BULLYING

Bullying is evil,
Bullying is sad,
The bully who does it,
Must be violent and mad.

Bullying is tragic,
People feel pain,
If you don't stop bullies,
The victim will go insane.

They may commit suicide,
They may hide in fear,
Then the bully will be prosecuted
And the crowds will cheer.

People may do drastic things
Or just stare in disgust,
The bully may get hurt but
People do what they must.

Overall, bullying is emotional,
It can make your life hell,
So don't just sit there,
Why don't you tell.

Beth Cooper (12)
Hope High School

BEDTIME

The moon is high,
The sun is low,
There's no one out,
No place to go.

All night long,
I've counted sheep,
I wish I was going off to sleep.

Then I got to that brilliant land,
Of sun, sea and golden sand.

It was not long till someone said,
'Hurry up,
You're late,
Get out of bed!'

Michael Lee Renshaw (14)
Hope High School

DEATH

The hour darkening, thunder rock heaven,
Lightning flashes upon a scene of carnage, blood and death,
Among the hundreds of bodies,
Was a man wearing a ripped cloak with his hood up,
His face covered in shadow, although his eyes shone like diamonds,
Gleaming a deep evil, blood red,
He was holding something which shone like the sun
Shining into an eternal darkness,
In the other hand was a wooden pole about four foot long,
With one end was a scythe blade glinting in the darkening hour.

Robert Vaughan (13)
Hope High School

THERE HE STANDS

There he stands, unknowing of my watchful eye.
His friends, ignorant of our ever-growing love,
Laugh and point over at our direction,
I have to shuffle back into the darkness of our love.

I look at him through the ever-growing pain in my heart,
His deep brown eyes catch my movement of pain,
Seeing the sensitive gaze in his eyes,
Melts away the dark shell which encloses me inside, alone.

I want to reach out and run my fingers through his spiky, black hair,
But my fingers are stricken with pain without his love.

So there he stands and must remain,
And I will have ever-growing pain,
There he stands.

Deena Fulton (15)
Little Lever School

SUMMER VS WINTER

It's the beginning of June,
The sun wakes me up, shining elegantly through my
Tightly drawn curtains.
I spring out of bed looking forward to the bright day ahead.
I gaze at the field, which is covered with beautiful glistening diamonds.
It's the beginning of January and all has changed,
I open my eyes and look around, everything is dark.
I crawl out of bed and try not to picture the dull day ahead.
I despair when I peak out of my window and see
The lifeless trees swaying in the cold winter wind.

Michael Norris (13)
Little Lever School

A BRILLIANT FAITHFUL MATE

Some people think it's loads of cash
That makes you feel great . . .
But what gives your life a better feeling
Is a brilliant faithful . . . *mate!*

Some people think tricking and bullying
Makes you feel good . . .
But what gives your life a better feeling
Is a brilliant faithful . . . *bud!*

Some people think stealing and dealing
Makes you feel special like a blue crystal . . .
But what gives your life a better feeling
Is a brilliant faithful . . . *pal!*

Some people think drinking and smoking
Is in the trend . . .
But what gives your life a better feeling
Is a brilliant faithful . . . *friend!*

And it's needless to say
It's true,
That a friend in need
Is a friend in deed.

Radhika Faldu (14)
Little Lever School

THE GREAT WAR '1914-1918'

That terrible day in history,
A captain once said.
'We'll accept nothing less than victory,'
As another man fell dead.

And when that man gets to Heaven,
To the great Lord he will tell,
'One more soldier reporting Sir,
'Cause I've served my time in Hell.'

Matthew Mitchell (15)
Little Lever School

KINGS AND RATS

The outcast;
The follower;
The combat-insane;
A childlike war,
On a war-torn plain.
His stars and his stripes,
Burdened with sins,
Fresh from the death,
Of his grand old twins.
As for the follower,
A leader, a fool,
To fight with your Saint,
A mockery most cruel.
The man with the secrets,
The man in the sand,
Sits on his throne,
The king of the land.
The moral of this,
Is be careful to choose,
Which king to keep
And which rat to lose.

David Pollitt (15)
Little Lever School

SOUTH OF THE WALLS WE FOUGHT

South of the walls we fought,
North of the ramparts we fell,
Fallen in the fields, graves non-existent,
Left to be eaten by the birds of sin.
Whisper a word in the raven's ear,
We are unafraid, courageous men far from home,
Fallen in the fields, graves non-existent,
How can our weary corpses escape you?

Find the place where the stream runs clear,
Where the reeds and rushes are midnight black,
Where the riders fought and were slain,
And their horses linger and call.

Upon the bridge there was a house -
How shall we cross?
North or south?
If the grain was never gathered,
What would we have to offer?
How shall our royal lord feast?
We wish to serve you,
But how can we succeed?

Our thoughts of you, brave soldiers,
Your service we will not forget:
At sunrise you charged into battle,
By sunset your seats were cold.

Laura Clarkson (15)
Little Lever School

In Memory Of Lia Sandford

It was a cold day in June, when Lia passed away.
Her warm smile and happy life sadly came to a finish.
She didn't deserve for her life to end so quickly
And painfully like it did.
In my eyes, she was always a survivor,
A friend everyone wishes for,
Someone to talk to, a shoulder to cry on,
But her happy life was up.
The cancer had gone too far.

The cancer hit her in the skin and fought against her
Until her strength to fight back vanished.
The cancer had won her over,
Took away her hair and her independence to live.
Seeing someone so helpless and sad I thought was only in dreams.
She had no hope.
The cancer had eaten away at my best friend and there was no possible
Way I was going to come to terms with it easily.

The life of my best friend Lia Sandford will always be one
That I will look back on with a tear.
How that strong, lively 17-year old girl's spirit wilted and died away.
I will always remember her as long as I shall live
And smile at the good times when she was able to laugh.
I thank God for giving me the bestest friend anybody
Could ever wish for!

Helen Matthews (15)
Little Lever School

BALLET

They told me it was easy,
My posture would be good,
With all the grace of an elephant,
I wish I only could.

My teacher smiles and says well done,
I know this should be fun,
But every time I go to class,
I get an aching bum!

My teacher recommended tap
Because my feet don't pointe,
The timing is a problem -
My feet just don't react.

Perhaps my forté isn't dance,
I'm not the type to prance,
I've now joined the local footie team,
I'm told I'm the dancing queen!

Katie Johnson (12)
Little Lever School

REFLECTION

The sunbeams danced across the room,
Motes of dust suspended in slow motion.
The mirror cracked, and thick with dust
My face surreal in reflection.
My eyes looked back, a familiar blue;
All said I looked like my mother.

Joanne Wainwright (15)
Little Lever School

CAN YOU GUESS WHAT I AM?

I am the rain pouring from the sky
I am the wind whistling in your ear
I am the sun glowing overhead
Can you guess what I am?

I am the snow that falls in winter
I am the coldness in the fresh air
I am the ice making you slip and slide
Can you guess what I am?

I work through the year, non-stop
I create the seasons, all four
I change all the time, each and every day
And I am totally unpredictable
Can you guess what I am?
I am the weather!

Jenna Cardell (11)
Little Lever School

PHOENIX

The singed grass, the black twigs,
The rain of fire from the phoenix.
A magnificent sight, an awesome swoop,
The dazzling flight of the phoenix.

A sort of flicker, a sort of flash,
You may just have seen the phoenix.
The strangest light, the dim glow,
The light at night from the phoenix.

Marcus Webb (12)
Little Lever School

WHAT A WONDERFUL WORLD

A girl I once knew died three years ago
The reason why nobody will ever know
Even though she is still breathing
Her forgotten grave still needs weeding
No one knows what's inside her head
There's only telltale scars on her wrist where she has bled
Behind false smiles she's learnt to hide
Hiding the fact that she's already died
She hears voices inside her head
Constant reminders of why she's now dead
Every scar she has tells a tale
Every goal set she seems to fail
In the darkness she thought she was lost forever
Till someone tried to put her life back together
Diagnosis: anxiety, depression no signs of aggression
Even they couldn't help her. Why not, it's her profession?
Reading another prescription for pills
Visible evidence of what she'd become gave her chills
Still it was too late, not enough will be left in her heart
It didn't take long till they gave up and she fell apart
The hatred inside her could drive some men to kill
Sometimes she hurts so much it makes her ill
The blood inside her runs ice-cold as it flows
As the seed of hate inside her grows
Her anger is shown by her icy glare
As the days go by she loses the will to care
Not that old but her nerves are frayed
In nine years to God not once has she prayed
In God she has lost all faith
Her whole life never again will she feel safe.

Kim Morris (15)
Little Lever School

GOD AND MAN

God and Man once had quite a relationship,
Before Man wrecked it,
God would create, and Man would thank,
God provided Man with the planet,
Then Man praised him for it.
God then created ocean, snow-tundra, desert and forest,
He gave them Dodo and Tasmanian Tiger,
The Man praised him for it.
And then God set Man free,
And Man too, started creating.
He created dams, guns, poison, cities,
He destroyed forest
And destroyed some ozone layer,
He wiped out Dodo and Tasmanian Tiger,
And God pitied him for it.
Even the cross of the church was subdued,
By the 'Golden Arches' of McDonald's,
Man only realised, when he found he wasn't happy.
He had no idea
And God pitied him for it.

Daniel Winward (16)
Little Lever School

SNOW

I woke up one morning and opened my curtains,
There before my eyes I saw
White, soft, light and smooth snow falling to the ground
As if a big white cloud has been popped in the sky,
It covered the floor in a thick white blanket,
It stayed there looking at me,
It was getting ready for me when had I woke up that morning.

Lyndsey Robishaw (13)
Little Lever School

A SENSE OF ARABIA

I rest for a moment:
Where a great almond tree throws its cool, dappled shadow.
I find it such a shock
To step out of the cool into the harsh light and scorching heat.
I begin to awaken to an entirely new form of beauty:
Soft reds and subtle lines
And yet, beneath the affluent exterior,
The essence and traditions of Arabia's people remain intact -
Deeply rooted in Islam.

Striking palaces edge tree-lined boulevards . . .
And yet it is to the older areas that I am repeatedly drawn.
A quiet, sandy lane between two high roads . . .
A woman glides by me,
Her dazzling, glorious jewels,
Swirling beneath the sombre enveloping abaya.
She lifts her hand to gather it around her,
A flash of gold bracelets sparkle out at me,
Adorning her henna-tipped fingers.
She is gone, leaving but her heavily exotic perfume
In her wake.
The more I see the more I begin to understand,
Yet in understanding,
I realise I am barely scratching the surface.

Kirsty Peploe (13)
Little Lever School

AUTUMN WIND

Spring is over, summer's gone
The autumn wind is very strong
Roads are empty, trees are bare
Brown, red and orange leaves are everywhere

The nights are darker, the days are longer
The autumn wind is getting stronger
Leaves are falling, twirling round
They slide down a tree branch and drop to the ground
The darkness is coming, light is gradually going
And still, the autumn wind keeps blowing.

Katy Howard (12)
Little Lever School

THE DRAGON

The great myth so great and tall,
The best part of a story most fearless of all,
Its dark slits in those huge scary red eyes,
Looking so angry as it sleeps there and lies,

Daring to go near its body so curvy,
If you're not too careful you will feel his full fury,
The room is lit by the fire it breathes,
Like breathing a light through those big frightening teeth,

He could crash down your house,
As easily as killing a mouse,
You are so puny while he stands there so great,
Fighting with him could bring you your fate.

As you fight for your life,
With your only weapon, a knife,
You aim for the heart, but the blade is too small,
So you stab with a sword that was hung on a wall.

The beast is once again laid,
The *dragon* has been slain.

Wayne Walsh (13)
Little Lever School

PARENTS GONE

I sit in my window at night,
Thinking how life would be
If only we had no parents,
We could do what we liked.

If I had no parents I would
Take care of my brother,
Go out where I wanted,
Watch whatever I want on TV.

But it would be hard work.
My brother would want endless money,
I would have to stay in to look after Leon,
I would also have to let Leon watch his things on the TV.

I'm glad I have parents,
To take care of me.
Without parents I'd be useless.

Nicola McGrady (11)
Little Lever School

BUT WHAT'S SO GOOD ABOUT BIKES THEN?

The endless treadmill of a road,
Providing space for the headlights disappearing behind us
And the brake lights appearing in front.

Accelerating like a bullet from a barrel,
Screeching round the tarmac track,
The road too close on corners
And the marks left from boots on the road.

Richard Gibbons (15)
Little Lever School

MY MISSING GRANDPARENTS

Sometimes I envy my friends
because they have grandparents.
Some of my friends have more than one
but I have none.

I have never seen my mum's parents
I have only seen one of my dad's
when I was very young.
I loved her to bits
and I cried when she died.

I miss the love and care
I miss the attention.
When my friends lose their grandparents
they will feel the same as I do.

Paul Armitage (13)
Little Lever School

AN ANGEL

Through the wispy clouds,
Into the blue sky,
An angel appears,
With glistening gold wings.
Her voice is gentle and quiet,
Her silky white dress flows.

At night she is still there,
Her voice still singing,
Protecting us over the still still night.
Always there.

Terri-Ann Worrall (12)
Little Lever School

THE WRAPPER

It was just lying there,
All on its own.
It has pink and silver colours
And a strawberry picture shown.
Someone had just opened it
And taken the sweet out.
Just left the wrapper lying there,
Oh what a lazy lout!
This just proved the laziness
Of mankind.
They start to use things
And leave a mess behind,
So that's the story of the wrapper,
Of a strawberry flavoured sweet.
I don't know why someone didn't throw it away
And left my *bedroom neat!*

Roxanna Lewis (13)
Little Lever School

LADIES IN WAITING

They hadn't sailed far at all,
Thirty knots was their maximum speed.
When the sky came down,
The wind whirled and wailed all around
And the sea grasped out for the vessel.

A long time, did the maidens sit,
With fine gowns of luxurious linen,
Their hair fell in glistening ringlets, down their backs,
But their faces were plagued with sorrow.
Tears made tracks down their flawless, milky-white skin.

They waited for their loved ones to return,
But their paths, would cross no more.
For half an hour out to sea,
Down, fifty feet deep.
There lay gallant Sir Orlando Rinaldi,
With the ladies and lords, at his feet.

Kirsty Gilchrist (13)
Little Lever School

THE ICKY VAN

The bell rings,
Girls and boys do naughty things.
Boys play football,
Girls learn netball.
Hear comes the icky van!
Some people get detention,
Others just want attention.
Years 10 and 11 scream,
But some are just plain mean.
Here comes the icky van!
People try to sneak inside,
They'll be lucky to stay alive.
Most boys end up in a fight,
Usually where it's not that light.
Here comes the icky van!

Finally it arrives
And even teachers come outside!

Sam Vause (11)
Little Lever School

BLOSSOMING FLOWERS

Look very closely,
At the flowers blooming,
Look how they lean,
Look very closely.

Look very carefully,
At the bright colours,
Look how they stand out,
Look very carefully.

Look at an angle,
Beyond the petals,
Look at its heart,
Look at an angle.

Look very closely,
Look very carefully,
Look at an angle,
Look at the blossoming flowers.

Helen Roscoe (14)
Little Lever School

FALLING STARS

If you look straight up
At the dark night sky
You will clearly see
A bright night star.

That bright night star
Will shine all around
It's light and glory
Of all the world.

That light and glory
Of all the world
Will keep us safe
From danger and harm.

Gary J Walters (11)
Little Lever School

I WONDER

The future, the future,
What is it like?
I wonder, I wonder,
What is it like?
Is it good, is it bad?
The future, the future,
What will it be like?

The past, the past,
What was it like?
I wonder, I wonder,
What was it like?
Was it good, was it bad?
The past, the past,
What was it like?

The present, the present,
I know what it's like.
No need to wonder,
I know what it's like.
It is good, it is bad,
The present, the present,
I know what it's like.

Tim Bartlett (11)
Little Lever School

WHY?

Let me take you by the hand
and lead you to that promised land.
Where cherry blossoms forever bloom
and rainbow flowers fill the room.
Where the weeping willows bow their heads
to a carpet of colour from blue to red.
The bluebells sway to a heartfelt tune
and the white bells watchful eyes the moon.
So as I look up to the sky I can't help but wonder why.
The world should be a happy place
standing side by side with the human race.
Then I see disaster fall,
two towers collapsed that once stood tall.
A city of hope now saying goodbye,
three minutes of silence a nation's cry.
So in years to come and times passed by
I'll still sit and wonder why.

Alan Simpson (12)
Little Lever School

MY FIRST DAY AT SCHOOL

I arrived at 8.30
I thought what a big school
Would I ever find my way around
Then the bell went
My heart was beating fast.

The hall was full of children
I remembered we all looked the same
Then I heard the teacher's voice
Then it went very quiet.

Off to my form room
Not knowing what was in store
Feeling a little unsure
Relax I was told.

Next thing I knew
Lunchtime was due
I felt much better
My first day was halfway through
Then the afternoon flew.

Jon-Paul Critchley (12)
Little Lever School

THE SHOW

I'm going to see the Red Hot Chili Peppers
And you're not.
I will be standing in line,
To see Anthony, John, Chad and Flea,
Waiting to mosh to Californiacation
And bounce round to Give It Away,
Then buy tacky merchandise at the end.
I'm going to see the Red Hot Chili Peppers
And you're not.

I'm going to see [spunge]
And you're not.
Going to see Alex, Wol, Des, Jarvis and Jem.
I'll be moshing to 'Ego'
And skankin' round for the rest of my livin'.

Daniel Povey (15)
Little Lever School

IS THIS MY FAULT?

I lie in silence in my room
Waiting for it to start again,
The screaming and shouting
Is this my fault?

Banging and crashing
Coming from downstairs,
Today has come again,
Today, tomorrow will it ever change?

I pull the cover over my head
To try and drown out the noise,
But it seems to be getting louder,
Is this my fault?

Why me?
Why my life?
Have I done something wrong?
Will I ever do anything right?

Screaming and shouting
Getting louder and louder,
What's going to happen?
Have I done something wrong?

Who's made them this way?
Is this my fault?
Will it ever change?
Please make it change.

I hear the noise coming up the stairs,
Is it going to be my turn now I wonder.
I can't take it any more,
I this my fault?

It must be my fault,
I have made them this way.
I wish it would just go away,
Go away, go away, leave me alone,
I can't take it any more!

Victoria Jayne Milton (14)
Little Lever School

SEASONS

It's summertime, it's hot and bright
Hooray there's not a cloud in sight
The birds are happy on this nice sunny day
As they watch the children dance and play.

Autumn comes around and the leaves begin to fall
There's a fluffy cat sat on the wall
The birds fly away to emigrate
The hedgehogs and badgers hibernate.

Winter's here, it's very cold
The snow is white and bright and bold
Santa comes on Christmas night
While Rudolph's nose is shining bright.

Spring comes around and the temperature rises
The gardens are alive and full of surprises
The birds return and build their nests
As the daffodils are at their very best.

Kimberley Hampson (12)
Little Lever School

THE DENTIST

Oh, my tooth, what a pain,
Off to the dentist yet again.
Sat in the waiting room full of fear,
How I wish I wasn't here.
Listening to the dreadful sound,
Of the drill going round.
Knowing my turn will soon come,
Now I wish I was at home.
It's my turn, he gave a shout,
He's going to take my teeth out.
He does it while I'm fast asleep,
While I'm busy counting sheep.
I wake up feeling a fool,
I make my way back to school.
All the pain has gone away,
And I can now enjoy my play.

Stacie Hayes (13)
Little Lever School

LOVE IS...

Love is sweet as sugar that melts in your mouth,
Love is complete, like a life lived to the full,
Love is time from you to me,
Love is a bond, so stick with me,
Love is divine, a passionate word,
Love is a gift of roses and flowers,
Love is filling and warm like a mug of hot chocolate,
Love is the thought that counts,
But most of all love is . . .

Iruka Eribenne (11)
Little Lever School

MY FIRST DAY

M y heart was beating madly,
Y ear 7s were scared to death,

F rightened of what the teachers will say,
I n the sports hall we all met on the first day,
R acing to the door, *not*
S tanding helplessly,
T rying to impress the teachers.

D aring not to say a word,
A nyway it was good in a way,
Y ours, Ashleigh Jade Storey.

Ashleigh Storey (11)
Little Lever School

FOOTBALL

I'm no good at football,
Or so my opponents wish.
I'm no good at passing
But I can put it on a dish.
I'm no good at dribbling,
They wish, they wish, they wish,
But I am good at winning,
I wish, I wish, I wish.

I wonder if they realise
I'm Pele in disguise!

Reuben Walters (11)
Little Lever School

I LOVE CATS

I love cats, they make me laugh.
I have three cats and they are daft.
Fidge is the oldest and she is black and white,
Sometimes she sleeps next door.
Tom's ginger and flops around the house.
Phoebe's brown and white and she is mad
And tries to get the budgies.
I've told you my cats are daft
And that's why I love them all.

Rebecca Walsh (11)
Little Lever School

SOMEONE SOMEWHERE

Someone somewhere
Dreams of your smile
And whilst thinking of you,
Says that life is worthwhile.
So when you're lonely
Remember it's true -
Someone somewhere is thinking about you.

Ali Hassan (14)
Little Lever School

BEGINNINGS AND ENDINGS

From the tiny caterpillar
to the beautiful butterfly.
From the cute little kitten
to the big, fluffy cat.
From the weak, little puppy
to the big, strong dog.

From the baby in arms
to the kind, loving grandma.
From tiny beginnings
to small, quiet endings.
From the smallest of creatures
to the biggest of them all.

Rachael Pollitt (11)
Little Lever School

THE LONE BOARDER

Hit the water as fast as I can.
Paddle deep, far out to sea;
Keep going 'til sunrise appears.
Saltwater cutting into my face.
Inhale deep before the lone stand;
Keep going, keep going! Don't lose it now.
Ride the galloping sea horse,
Take the reins now!

Sam Dry (12)
Little Lever School

OUR NEW HOME

When we first moved in,
The house was thick with dust
And all the pipes,
Were full of rust.
The house was cold,
The curtains were worn
And nobody had bothered
To mow the garden lawn.

Cara Lomas (14)
Little Lever School

ROWING, ROWING

Rowing, rowing,
Night and day,
Feeling pain as whips were laid
Mid Atlantic,
No escape.
Blazing sun
We had to stand,
Peeling backs
Can't wait for land.
Land ahoy, oh land ahoy,
Still chained we walk ashore,
The auctioneer, awaiting
Two pounds, we were worth more.

Paul Davies (13)
Little Lever School

WALKING

When I was walking the other day,
I thought about the things I love,
Like the birds and trees,
The wasps and the bees.

I then looked up in the sky
To see geese flying by,
The leaves were shuffling along the ground,
The flowers sat there waving their petals around.

These are the things I see every day,
Wild and free.

Katie Whitehead (12)
Little Lever School

MY PENCIL CASE

My pencil case
Black as night
Filled with objects
That help me write
Pens, pencils
Rubbers and glue
Black pens, blue pens
All types of gel pens
I use it when I'm at school
I use it when I'm at home
My pencil case is full to the top
It's almost bursting the zip open
Three years old
It's still in use.

Mark Howarth (13)
Little Lever School

IF ONLY THEY KNEW

The sun shone down on the field where the sheep were grazing,
If only they knew.
Dust rose from the lane as the lorry arrived,
If only they knew.
The dog began to shepherd them together,
If only they knew.
The gate opened and they were herded towards the lorry,
If only they knew,
If only they knew they would never see the sun shine again.

Emma Holland (13)
Little Lever School

THE POT

Round about the cauldron go,
In peacock's feathers throw.
Mix it up with bear's ear and scorpion's sting,
Rabbit's tail and owl's wing.

Round and round it all goes,
Making everyone hold their nose
So then they throw in a rose.

Eye of frog,
Tail of cat.
Wool of sheep,
Mouth of rat,
Human hand and head of man,
Mix it up with guts of ram.

Round and round it all goes,
Making everyone hold their nose
So then they throw in a rose.

All the stripes of the tiger
And a mouse drinking cider.
Now put in a fillet of snake,
Then let it boil or bake.

Kirsty McCaig (11)
Little Lever School

THE WORLD TO ME

Through the window I see
How the world should be.
A smile for you, a smile for me,
Through the window I see

Through the door I hear
A whisper in my ear,
A world without fear,
Through the door I hear.

Through the shadows I know
Happiness from head to toe,
A world with friend and no foe,
Through the shadows I know.

Through the light I see
A world of poverty,
This is the way the world should not be,
Through the light I see.

In the future I know
That there will be happiness
From head to toe
And the world will glow,
In the future I know.

Jessica Clarke (12)
Little Lever School

BEWARE OF THE TOOTH FAIRY

This rhyme is a tale of a fairy,
Not unlike many old fairy tales.
But reader take care and be wary,
For fairies are harder than nails.

We meet at the start of our poem,
A 5 year old boy known as Ben
And Ben has a brother called Owen,
But Owen's much older - he's 10.

Now Ben had a problem with teeth,
He just couldn't make them fall out,
So that new teeth could grow underneath
And that's what our tale's all about.

When chatting to young chums at school,
Our 5 year old hero had found,
In return for a tooth - as a rule,
The tooth fairy left you a pound.

The young chaps would go on and on,
About what they would do with their pound
And as soon as the money had gone,
Another tooth wobbled around.

As schoolchildren's teeth fell out daily,
Teeth of all kinds of size and shape,
When it happened the teachers would mainly,
Stick lost teeth to their desk with some tape.

Attached to each tooth was a label,
So that each child knew which was their gem,
They remained there stuck to the table,
Till home time at 4pm.

Jenni Clarkson (14)
Little Lever School

I WISH . . .

I wish I was a monkey
I could swing high up in the trees
I could be the king of the jungle
I could eat bananas all day long
Actually I couldn't because I don't like bananas.

I wish I was a tiger
I could prowl through the grass in search of prey
I could be the king of the jungle
I could eat the meat of my prey all day long
Actually I couldn't because I don't like raw meat.

I wish I was a dolphin
I could swim through the sea
I could be the queen of the sea
I could eat fish all day long
Actually I couldn't because I don't like fish.

I wish I was a horse
I could gallop through the field
I could be queen of the field
I could eat grass all day long
Actually I couldn't because I don't like grass.

Maybe I should be me
I can play with my mates
I can be the king of the climbing frame all day long
I can eat my mum's cooking
Yeah I think that's what I want to do.

Rachael Williams (11)
Little Lever School

ZEBRA

Stripy zebra
Stays still and suspicious,
Looks alert,
Timid and scared
In the bone dry sun
Under the wrecked trees,
Lion watching,
Strong lion staring,
Zebra stiff with fear,
Lion pounces,
Zebra leaps and jumps
In the red-hot sun,
Gallops away into the trees.

Anthony Gibson (13)
Marland Fold Special School

MERRY MILLENNIUM?

Monkeys with mobile phones swinging through the trees.
Internet teachers ignoring ignorant infants.
Lazy lions lying in the sun.
Large lemons sweet but not sour.
Endangered Eskimos eat eels to stay alive.
Nutty gnomes knock on doors.
Electric eels illuminate, excited about everything.
Unknown unicorns upspring into the air.
Memory loss and mighty missiles missing the Millennium Dome.

Peter Webster (18)
Marland Fold Special School

LOVE

It may not be great,
Some think it's a joke,
It's different in its own way.

It can hurt,
It can be fun,
It can be painful.

Treat it how you want,
But I'll give you some advice,
If I was you I'd treat it with care,
Be proud of it while you can
Or it will backfire on you.

I'll tell you what it's called,
Go on have one more guess.
OK, I'll tell you,
It's the greatest thing that could happen to some,
It's called *love!*

Gemma Crozier (13)
Queen's Park Technology College

SUNSET!

The sun is setting,
All the colours shining bright,
The oranges, reds, yellows and pinks,
All so beautiful and at the same time so still and quiet.
It is impossible to describe what the feeling is,
It is not hot but not cold.
The sun has nearly set
And it's nearly time for the full, bright white moon to shine
Its full strength!

Danielle Hobson (13)
Queen's Park Technology College

MY DAD'S A DOG!

One day I just had my tea
I looked at my dad,
He had a flea,
I said to him, 'Get some spray
And the flea might go away.'
So he went outside to the shed,
I stared at him,
Then he said,
'Come here, come here,
I need your help.'
'No,' I said with a yelp,
'I might catch something
You've got.'
'No you won't,' he said to me,
'You're not the one
Who's got a flea.'

Leeann Wilcock (13)
Queen's Park Technology College

A CHILD'S DREAM

As she slept, her dreams began
Of elegant ponies and giant castles
And huge chariots with silver tassels,
Oh what fun!
As he slept, his dreams began
Of super speed cars and huge mansions
And maybe having one or two extensions,
Oh what fun!
As their dreams began to expire
The children know what they desire.

Mohammed Irfan Bhai (13)
Queen's Park Technology College

THE TOWERS

As the towers collapsed
and the crowds dispersed.

A loud rumble was heard
as a state was cursed.

Death by the thousands
those little cowards they hide.

We'll search the world over
both far and wide until we find them.

Then justice is served
as we watch them whine in the jail.

For God is the judge,
His power will be strong to decide if they will die.

William Hudson (13)
Queen's Park Technology College

SCHOOL

It's boring!
And our school teacher is snoring.
Every time he wakes up
His glasses fall off,
He goes and jumps on the table top
And thinks he can fly.

We just wish that he'd go back to sleep,
At least he won't scream again
When he's sleeping, at least he won't peep,
Watching us run around the whole laboratory game.

Romila Ashraf (14)
Queen's Park Technology College

AS THE CLASS BELL RANG

As the class bell rang
I knew I was late,
I jumped into class
And sat next to my mate.

The teacher ran in
Pantin' an' puffin'
She stared at me
As I finished my muffin.

Her face went red
With jealousy I thought,
But she proved me wrong
As she passed me a note.

As I read the note
It was a note for detention,
It had said that
I had not paid much attention.

My hands were trembling,
I didn't know what to do,
Then a voice in my head said,
It's not for you.

As I looked at the top
It was not for me,
It was for John left-hander
In class CE.

When I told the teacher
She gave me a nice look,
Then she threw me out of the class
For not reading my history book.

Mehreen Solkar (13)
Queen's Park Technology College

MARY DELANEY

Mary Delaney comes to school,
With a mouth as wide as a swimming pool,
Eyes like a frog,
And ears like a bat
And hair like the tail of an old tomcat.

She always smiles like an alligator,
Her breath smells of garlic and mashed potato!
She's nice to children
But cruel to dogs
She makes Jack Russells into chocolate logs!

She has a brother, who has two double chins,
One set of triplets
And one set of twins,
She has a dad, who's an orang-utan,
All fierce and firm,
But her mum is a reptile,
That makes Mary squirm.

Mary Delaney's first friend is Joan,
She's always the first ever to moan,
Her second friend his name is Fred
All he eats is jam and bread.

Mary Delaney (11)
St Edmund Arrowsmith RC High School, Wigan

PIKE

Pike, pike
Mammal eater
Camouflaged fighter
Black, evil fish.

Paul Jones (13)
St Edmund Arrowsmith RC High School, Wigan

THE PORCUPINE

A porcupine so cute and small,
It curls up into a little ball.
Its beady-eyes, its little nose,
It's very cute you would suppose.

Now do be careful not to touch
Because it can hurt you very much.
Needles that are strong as steel,
Do be careful where you kneel.

They can stab you they're so sharp,
They could pierce you in the heart.
This porcupine so cute and small
Isn't really cute at all.

Francesca Kerfoot (12)
St Edmund Arrowsmith RC High School, Wigan

THE KING OF THE JUNGLE

They call him the King of the Jungle,
With his great sharp claws.
Oh his huge big paws
Help him hunt his prey.

Everyone looks up to him
Like the beast that he is,
Probably scared of
The King of the Jungle.

David Houghton (12)
St Edmund Arrowsmith RC High School, Wigan

CUDDLES

I have a little bunny rabbit,
It's only a teddy bear,
But as I climb the stairs at night
It's waiting for me there.

I cuddle my little bear at night,
It's as cuddly as can be,
I love my little bear to bits
But does it really love me?

And in the morning as I wake up
And look to my left and look to my right
I see my cuddly teddy bear,
The one I cuddled all night.

Catherine Sweeney (12)
St Edmund Arrowsmith RC High School, Wigan

HALLOWE'EN!

Witches, wizards and ghosts too
Will scare the life out of you.
Zombies rising from the dead
And nightmares crashing in your head.
Mummies awaken from their tomb
And a noise around you goes doom, doom, *doom!*

Spiders crawl along the floor
And a monster is knocking at your door.
You open the door and look down the street
And then they all chorus *trick or treat!*

Rachel Heard (12)
St Edmund Arrowsmith RC High School, Wigan

THE WORLD

Where did we come from?
How were we made?
Why do we behave
How we want to?

When were we created?
When did time begin?
Who lived first?
When did we get here?

Are we alone?
Do we live in peace?
Can we do the impossible?
If so, how do we know?

So many mysteries,
Probably never to be solved.
Can we ever tell
What's to become of us?

Nathan O'Leary (12)
St Edmund Arrowsmith RC High School, Wigan

THE CROCODILE

He thrives on land and sea
And is a deadly hunter.
He seems so still and then you're dead,
You're without your head.
But you have to admire this beautiful creature
For he is so very old
And if you see past those deadly jaws
He has one dinosaur of a mould.

Jonathan Frayne (12)
St Edmund Arrowsmith RC High School, Wigan

WHAT IS A BABY?
(For Elle-Marie)

What is a baby . . . ?

A baby is a shining star that twinkles in the sky,
It laughs and dribbles nearby.

It has tiny fingers and tiny toes
And a little button nose.

A baby's laugh tickles my tummy
As it's laughing at its daddy and mummy.

It soon falls into a dreamy sleep
With no crying or a weep.

Its mummy puts it to bed,
There it rests its sleepyhead.

Rebecca Kennedy (12)
St Edmund Arrowsmith RC High School, Wigan

NIGHTMARE

I sat in bed one cold night
And clutched my favourite teddy tight,
I heard creaky noises on the floor
But I was too scared to open my door,
The hairs on my back started to stand,
It felt like I could feel every strand.
As my eyes opened I started to peer
And I felt the warmth of a single tear,
I couldn't see anything there that night
But one thing's for sure it gave me a fright.

Danielle Holmes (12)
St Edmund Arrowsmith RC High School, Wigan

MAGIC BOX
(Based on The Magic Box by Kit Wright)

Inside my magic box
There are memories unforgotten.
The sides are woven from dreams,
The lid crafted from friendship and loyalty.
The lock is moulded from secrets untold,
The hinges shaped from help and care.
In the corners though, lurks fear and fright
And worries, envy and hate,
But happiness inside my box
Will never let out the worries and hate,
Shutting them away and pushing them into corners
And when I close my magic box
I lock inside all the help and love and joy,
To keep, forever.

Catherine Byrne (12)
St Edmund Arrowsmith RC High School, Wigan

THE CAT

The creature of the night,
        eyes of glowing light bulbs.
It slyly stalks its prey then
        pounces like a tiger.
Its delicate whiskers can detect
        any danger from all round approaching
And its sharp claws protect
        this creature.
During the cold winter nights
        its little ears prick up.
This creature is the cat
        and she's all mine.

Alexandra Gribbon (12)
St Edmund Arrowsmith RC High School, Wigan

SANTA CLAUS

At 6 o'clock on Christmas morning
When I get up and I start yawning,
Everyone's asleep in bed
But I'm searching for my moped.
I hear a noise from up the chimney
But I just think it must be me,
The Christmas tree lights flash on and off
And then I hear someone cough.
'All this soot is giving me a rash
And I haven't got any cash.
I save up for Christmas every year
Then I've no money for my beer.'
'Hurry up,' I hear someone say,
'I'm getting tired of pulling this sleigh.'
He tiptoed very quietly
And hid the presents under the tree.

Peter Langley (11)
St Edmund Arrowsmith RC High School, Wigan

MY DOGS

Fluffy, warm and cuddly too,
My dogs play and play fight too,
They mostly sleep and eat all day,
Then they go and down they lay,
Morning comes and up they get,
They see their dinner and then they eat,
They finish and walk around,
They see us in the background,
They brought their ball and came to play
So we played and played and played all day.

Michelle Hewitt (11)
St Edmund Arrowsmith RC High School, Wigan

CAT

God made creatures
Great and small,
We all think ours
Is best of all;
Mine's a thinker,
He sits and stares
Waiting and waiting with every purr,
Feel sorry for me
Is in his glare;
He's waiting for
The moment when
He can pounce on his prey.
With that seemingly effortless efficiency;
As if he cares
But I know deep down;
He is just a
Pussy cat.

Samantha Atherton (12)
St Edmund Arrowsmith RC High School, Wigan

THE STARS

Stars, stars way up in the sky,
Beautiful and bright shining through the night.
They come out on the still, calm nights,
Even on the rough, thundery nights.
So if you ever feel lonely or sad
Look at the stars and they'll make you feel glad.

Alexis Cahillane (13)
St Edmund Arrowsmith RC High School, Wigan

THE CAT

I looked out my window
And in the midst of the night
A black creature slowly moves;
Its eyes shining,
Its claws scraping,
Then faster and faster it moves
And with one great pounce
It catches its prey.
It looks up and I glance at it
And it stares with its suspicious eyes,
Then quickly it runs
Over the garden fence and out of sight.

Laura Buckley (12)
St Edmund Arrowsmith RC High School, Wigan

CHEETAH

As quick as lightning,
As ruthless as a bear,
With claws like saws,
He strikes!
Rips his prey apart
And leaves his heart.
He spots a seedling,
It starts bleeding.
Round the bend
Hyenas ascend,
They rip it apart
But the hyenas
Cut its heart.

Daniel Meyrick (11)
St Edmund Arrowsmith RC High School, Wigan

A Voice Inside Of Me

In my mind I can hear
A conscience so clear
Telling me I'm a disaster,
Making me feel ever so bad.

In my mind I can imagine
The kindest, most peaceful place.
This world can't compete to
That special place.

I wondered what the world
Would be like without me,
Would it be better?
Would it be worse?

Now in reality I feel
Lucky to have friends
And family that surround me.
And now I'm whole
And not a lonely soul.

Laura Smallshaw (12)
St Edmund Arrowsmith RC High School, Wigan

Special

S   omeone special is my mum,
P   roven she is number one,
E   xample of someone so charming and great,
C   heerful and lovely, she's my best mate,
I   f I have a problem that comes with a frown,
A   lways she'll help when I'm feeling down,
L   ike her there is no one who'll pair
    with someone so kind, so generous, so rare.

Corrina Connor (11)
St Edmund Arrowsmith RC High School, Wigan

SPIDERS

Creep and crawl
That's what spiders do,
They hang around on webs
Ready to scare you!

Creep and crawl,
Thousands of staring eyes,
In the bath and in the corner
The dreaded thing lies.

Creep and crawl,
Long black legs
So hairy,
Spiders come out to scare me.

Creep and crawl,
Waiting to catch a fly,
Terrifying me as I walk by.

Creep and crawl,
My worst fear,
I'll never like spiders
And I'll never go near.

Katie Simpkin (11)
St Edmund Arrowsmith RC High School, Wigan

SHARKS

S   wimming around without any sleep,
H   ellraisers of the deep,
A   ll day long, hunting for food,
R   olling red eyes,
K   id eater,
S   erial killer.

Andrew Price (11)
St Edmund Arrowsmith RC High School, Wigan

DOGS

A fast runner,
A food lover.

I'll sleep later,
A cat hater.

A ball chaser,
A running racer.

A growl and a bark,
A good walk in the park.

Likes a good swim,
Makes a big din.

Their energy never ends,
A man's best friend.

Lea Kirsty Davies (11)
St Edmund Arrowsmith RC High School, Wigan

CAT

Paw-padder,
Mouse-muncher,
Dog-hater,
Bird-killer,
Tree-climber,
Wood-scratcher,
Sofa-shredder,
Fish-eater,
String-fighter,
Human-lover.

Steven Abbott (11)
St Edmund Arrowsmith RC High School, Wigan

A FAMILY!

A family sticks together,
Together we will stick,
We are one family
Who love one another,
We worship each other,
We care for each other,
We think about each other,
We pray for each other
Every day and every night,
A beautiful bond keeps us together,
We think about each other every day,
If someone gets hurt
We pray,
We are glad that God made us
One perfect family!

Rebecca Aldred (12)
St Edmund Arrowsmith RC High School, Wigan

WHEN I GO TO SCHOOL

When I go to school
I look out for my friends.

When I go to school
I use up all my spends.

When I go to school
I wait for the bell to go.

When the bell has gone
I just go with the flow.

Bradley Simm (11)
St Edmund Arrowsmith RC High School, Wigan

WHAT IS A MUMMY?

What is a mummy?
This is what you think while you suck your dummy,
Nice, snug and warm in your baby blanky,
People come, people go, saying, 'Don't you look just like
                                    your mummy.'
There's that word again, mummy, what could it be?

Wa, wa,
Suck, suck,
Shh, shhh,
What could a mummy be?

What is a mummy? You dream in your dream,
Maybe it's a teddy, maybe it's a dummy, maybe it's a team.
You fall into your never-ending dream,
Dreaming what is a mummy, mummy, mummy, mummy?

Wa, wa,
Suck, suck,
Shh, shh,
What could a mummy be?

Who is this person who looks just like me?
Who is this person who watches over me?
Who is this person who says what a beautiful sight?
Who is this person who sleeps next to me?
'Hello darling, I'm your mummy!' this person says.
Some people say she's my mother, some people say she's my mummy,
But all I can say is . . .
She is mine, my own special mummy!

Amy Wood (11)
St Edmund Arrowsmith RC High School, Wigan

GROOVY CHICK

She's funny, she's happy,
She's very, very mad!
She's pretty, she's popular
And never ever sad!

She wears lipstick and blusher
And sets the latest trend!
She's polite, she's clever
And has the greatest friends!

She's trusting and worthy,
She never ever lies!
She always has a spare shoulder
To help a friend who cries!

She's nice and quiet in class
And never ever talks!
She helps the teacher when he tries
To find the coloured chalks!

A 'groovy chick' cannot be found
In every single school!
But the school she likes the most is . . .
St Edmund Arrowsmith, cool!

So can you guess who she is,
Who sings so happily?
Of course, it's obvious!
The very groovy *me!*

Tamara Cunningham (11)
St Edmund Arrowsmith RC High School, Wigan

THE MOON

I lay on the grass
And stare up through the misty gloom.
Shining brightly
I see the moon.

Its glowing surface
Shining bright,
Staring down,
Down on the Earth all night.

When the mist cleared
With the windy breeze.
I wondered
Is it made of cheese?

Or maybe smiling
With the man in the moon,
Enjoying the life
Until the noon.

When I knew I could relax
And lie on the plain,
I knew the moon was watching,
Never to be dark again.

Joshua Fulton (11)
St Edmund Arrowsmith RC High School, Wigan

MY BIRDS

Tweet, tweet, tweet
As my little birds eat.
Tickles and Doble
Always peck at my bobble.

Every day my friends will say,
'Are you coming out to play?'
But I say, 'No,
I have to go
And spend some time with my birds.'

Kendra McCormack (11)
St Edmund Arrowsmith RC High School, Wigan

SCHOOL HOLIDAYS

I like school holidays
They're so much fun.

I like school holidays,
Just playing in the sun.

I like school holidays,
Staying with my dad.

I like school holidays
Because I'm so glad.

I like school holidays,
Playing with my friends.

I like school holidays,
Blowing all my spends.

I like school holidays,
Teenagers staying sober.

I like school holidays,
But not when it's over.

Steven Cahill (11)
St Edmund Arrowsmith RC High School, Wigan

THE NIGHTMARE

I am asleep in the middle of the night
And then I see something that gives me a fright,
It looks so real or so it seems,
Its face is wrinkled and very unclean.

I can't move and I can't scream,
Something is stopping me, it's being so mean,
It walks closer and closer with every glide,
I'm so scared - I want to hide.

It circles me for ages - I don't know what to do,
It's saying nasty words at me like *cheater, scam* and *boo!*
I wake up with a fright,; my mum is sitting there,
'Get up, or you'll be late,' she says and fiddles with my hair.

I never saw that thing again; I hope I never will,
It's big and scary and very mean - I think it went through the mill,
But now I know never to do horrible things in the day,
Because it comes back to you, in your dreams in a very different way.

Emma Ashcroft (12)
St Edmund Arrowsmith RC High School, Wigan

AUTUMN

As the leaves fall off the trees,
As the winter weather comes,
The snow, ice and rain
Take a grasp on part of the world.

As the long days turn to short ones
And the hot nights become cold,
People descend to the indoors
Because autumn has come here.

Philip Naugton (11)
St Edmund Arrowsmith RC High School, Wigan

AT THE END OF AN ASSEMBLY

Miss Sparrow's lot flew out,
Mr Bull's lot got herded out,
Mrs Steed's lot galloped out,
Miss Bumble's lot buzzed off.

Miss Rose's class rose,
Mr Beetle's class beetled off,
Mrs Storm's lot thundered out,
Miss Frisby's lot whirled across the hall.

Mr Ferry's lot sailed off,
Miss Train's lot made tracks,
Mr Roller's lot got their skates on,
Mrs Street's class got stuck halfway across.

Mr Idle's lot couldn't be bothered,
Mrs Barrow's class were wheeled out,
Miss Stretcher's lot got carried out
And Mr Brook's lot simply trickled away.

Laura Davis (12)
St Edmund Arrowsmith RC High School, Wigan

MY DOG

My dog is a pain,
It drives me insane.
All it does is bark
Even when we go to the park.

It pulls me all around the block
And runs off with my socks.
Although my dog is still cute,
At times I wish she was a mute.

Rebecca Waring (11)
St Edmund Arrowsmith RC High School, Wigan

SEASONS

Spring
The flowers are growing,
The bees are buzzing,
Lambs baaing,
The sun shining.

Summer
Red-hot days,
Sizzling sun,
Dogs are panting,
Summer fun.

Autumn
Red and gold leaves,
Cold in your bed,
Squirrels search for nuts,
Collecting conkers from trees.

Winter
The icy weather,
Snowball fights,
Hats and scarves,
Snowy sights.

Lauren McCormack (11)
St Edmund Arrowsmith RC High School, Wigan

EARLY SUNDAY MORNING

Early Sunday morning
When the birds begin to sing
And the milk bottles on the milk float clang and ding,
I lay in my bed all warm and snug
With a big fluffy teddy that I like to hug.

Hayley Keough (11)
St Edmund Arrowsmith RC High School, Wigan

MY DREAM SCHOOL

My dream school can be
Anything really.
I wish my dreams would
Come true ever so really.

My dream school
Could be based in a large swimming pool,
Where we can have fun
In the hot burning sun.

My dream school could be
A theme park,
So we could stay out
Until it gets dark.
We can have lessons on the rides,
Have play times on the big slides.

My dream school can be
Anything really!

Hannah Turner (11)
St Edmund Arrowsmith RC High School, Wigan

MY BED

Warm and gentle, fluffy and light,
It waits for me there every night.
Comfy and relaxing, it's always just right,
It's always in the mood when I want a pillow fight.
I walk through the door and what do I see?
My great big bed smiling at me!

Jessica Seddon (11)
St Edmund Arrowsmith RC High School, Wigan

My Dad

My dad is super cool,
We do everything together,
From swapping jokes to shooting pool,
He says he'll love me forever.

My dad is like a superman,
He teaches me about his job,
Not just that but all he can,
He talks to me when I'm in a sob.

Batman and Robin is me and Dad,
The unstoppable daring crew.
I truly am his favourite lad,
He would die for me, yes it's true.

So for now my dad
I'd like to say,
I'll love you till my dying day.

Billy Howells (11)
St Edmund Arrowsmith RC High School, Wigan

My Nightmare

N early every night they come,
I run and run but get nowhere.
'G o away, go away,' I shout.
'H elp, help,' I cry and cry
     but no one's there to help me by.
T oss and turn in a cold wet sleep,
M oaning, wailing that's what I do.
A nightmare is an evil monster,
'R oar, roar,' I hear it say.
E very night I lie there scared.

Greg McDonald (11)
St Edmund Arrowsmith RC High School, Wigan

MY SIMILE POEM

Kayne Craven runs to class
Trying to find his bus pass.
Hair like hay and skin like bark,
His favourite bird is a skylark.

His pants are grey and his blazer's green,
When he's angry he's mean.
His head is hollow,
When he eats he just swallows.

His grandma watches Poirot,
His sister wants his PlayStation to borrow.
His dad works at Heinz,
His mum likes furniture made from pines.

His best mate John is wacky,
His other mate Scott is snappy.
His dog is really big,
His polecat plays tig.

Kayne Craven (11)
St Edmund Arrowsmith RC High School, Wigan

FOOTBALL

F   ootball is the greatest sport,
O   f course it's better than tennis on the court.
O   n the pitch come all the players,
T   ourists coming from all over the world.
B   alls being shot into the nets,
A   ll the fans making bets.
L   ots of tickets being sold,
L   ate it is, the match is coming to an end.

Jamie Richards (12)
St Edmund Arrowsmith RC High School, Wigan

The Deep Blue Sea

Down in the darkness of the deep blue sea
Live many little creatures not at all like you and me.
Some have eight legs and some have none at all,
Some are very big and some are very small.
Predators hunt with their eyes open wide,
Searching for their food underneath the moving tide.
Schools of fish are glistening in the light,
Not knowing what beasts will come for them in the night.
Morning breaks and the dolphins come out,
They begin to jump and splash about.
Not a care in the world, they play all day,
Diving down a long, long way.
The deep blue sea is a really cool place,
It's so much better than being out in space.

Charlotte Heaton (11)
St Edmund Arrowsmith RC High School, Wigan

Orange And Yellow

It's orange and yellow
Like a comfy marshmallow.
It's a place to eat,
A really special treat.
It's a box of emotion,
Laughter, sadness and commotion.
So, what could it be?
This thing so special to me.
Where at night do I lay my head?
Why, of course, on my orange and yellow bed!

Erin Anne McVitie (11)
St Edmund Arrowsmith RC High School, Wigan

SIOBHAN O'GARA

Siobhan O'Gara runs into class
And the teacher yells, 'You've missed the mass!'
She runs on legs like short tree stumps
And her messy bedroom is filled with junk.
Lips as dark as a red, red rose,
When it comes to modelling she can strike a pose!
Her eyes are as green as a fresh, young leaf,
Her sister has hair like a coral reef.
She can't knit wool and she can't sew,
She has skin as white as snow.
Her mum is short,
Her dad is tall,
Her sister's a bully
And to them she's small.

Siobhan O'Gara (11)
St Edmund Arrowsmith RC High School, Wigan

ALONG THE SEASHORE

I love the beaches
Beaches have greeny-blue seas
Seas have turquoise seaweed
Seaweed is squashed between rocks
Rocks hide small sea creatures
Creatures as small as snails
Snails slither along the shore
Shore breezes whistle through the palms
Palms shade the hot sand
Sand is golden yellow
Yellow as the sun.

Samantha Sheehan (11)
St Edmund Arrowsmith RC High School, Wigan

MY SIMILE POEM

Shane Jones comes to class
Holding a big pint glass,
Stealing people's money
And he thinks it's very funny,
What a boy is that Shane Jones!

His mum has completely lost control
Because all Shane does is rock and roll.
Shane's dad is sick and tired
Of the amount of birds that have been fired.

Shane's sister's pulling her hair out,
She does hate Shane without a doubt.
His grandma and grandad lose their patience the most,
Shane acts like they're just ghosts.

Oh! That Shane Jones he tries his best
To put his parents to the test.

Shane Jones (12)
St Edmund Arrowsmith RC High School, Wigan

MY NEW SCHOOL

The gates swung and banged,
The bin rolled around on the floor
Like a steamroller hunting to crush its prey.
Schoolgirl's laughs echoed in the wind,
Suddenly the doors of the old, dilapidated school crashed open
And there stood a tall, dark figure,
The principal.

Joshua Glover (11)
St Edmund Arrowsmith RC High School, Wigan

ELIZABETH GARDENER

Lizzy comes to school
And she's very cool.
Ears like elves',
Tall like holes in wells
And a little squashed nose
On her face.

My dad is very tall
And my mum is quite small.
My brothers and sister are all the same
And my dad gets mixed up with all their names.

She tries her best
And is a pest
And never gets things right,
You want to see her in the morning,
She will give you a fright.

Elizabeth Gardener (11)
St Edmund Arrowsmith RC High School, Wigan

THE LAND OF SLEEPING DREAMS

In the land of sleeping dreams
Flowers blossom,
Birds sing,
Water flows from pool to pool,
All our dreams, our hopes come true,
Magical lands never-ending
Until the dawn's rays shine,
The land of children ending
Until the night again will fall.

Jennifer Blackburn (11)
St Edmund Arrowsmith RC High School, Wigan

STARTING HIGH SCHOOL

Looking around it's all big and new,
When the bell goes we all line up in a queue.

It's scary not knowing anyone at all
And all the other years are so tall.

It's totally different from my old primary school,
If you fall over you just get called a fool.

After a few weeks you get used to the fuss,
At last it's home time, time for the bus.

Louise Wood (11)
St Edmund Arrowsmith RC High School, Wigan

DREAMS

Some dreams are sweet
Like having a treat.

Some dreams are so scary
Like monsters big and hairy.

Most are welcome and warm
So I sleep until dawn.

When I wake up in the morning
I don't seem to be yawning.

When I think about the wonderful dream,
It was so good like fresh cream.

Emma-Jane Leyland (11)
St Edmund Arrowsmith RC High School, Wigan

THE VICTIM

Slithering on the dusty ground
Until the destination is found.
On the floor the victim lies dead,
The predator waits patiently until he is fed.

His mouth opens very wide
And his heart fills with joy and pride.
Slowly the victim slides down his throat,
You can see its mould through the snake's coat.

The snake curls up and goes to sleep,
He doesn't open his eyes not even a peep.
Sssssssss!

Rachael Edwards (12)
St Edmund Arrowsmith RC High School, Wigan

DREAMS!

I go to bed and close my eyes
And drift into my dream,
They have a beginning
And sometimes no end,
They're not always what they seem.

I've dreamt in colour
And black and white,
I like the good dreams best of all,
Not the ones that give you a *fright!*

Rachel Ashurst (11)
St Edmund Arrowsmith RC High School, Wigan

HORSE

H ollie is the best,
O pen fields full of grass,
L ong slimy tongue licks my hand,
L ovely, soft and sensitive,
I love her, she is the best pet to have,
E very day she gallops in the field.

T oday she is being clipped,
H air falls to the ground,
E very day I put her rug on.

H ollie loves to let me ride her,
O pen the stable door, then get her saddle,
R ide round the paddock, walk, trot, canter,
S low down because she is sweaty,
E very day I love my horse, Hollie.

Hannah Hughes (12)
St Edmund Arrowsmith RC High School, Wigan

TROUBLE

T errified of teachers.
R olling on the ground.
O ut to find trouble is my game.
U nable to be good.
B eing bad is my thing.
L eaning over the table chatting to my friends.
E arwigging conversations.

Thomas Corsair (11)
St Edmund Arrowsmith RC High School, Wigan

My Dogs

M y dogs, one is called Simba,
Y ou see them as quite sweet.

D on't go too close
O r they bark.
G ood boy Simba, good girl,
S o special to me.

A re you sure you want a bone?
R eady, steady fetch,
E asy, peasy dogs.

T hey are good dogs,
H ere boy, here girl,
E asy-peasy dogs.

B est
E ver,
S o sweet,
T he end.

Lauren Holcroft (11)
St Edmund Arrowsmith RC High School, Wigan

Dogs

D is for disgrace when he's got mud on his face.
O is for oversized paws that really dig in.
G is for gruesome when he bites at your chin.
S is for sausages that he gets out of the bin.

Daniel Hull (11)
St Edmund Arrowsmith RC High School, Wigan

GABRIELLE HARRISON

Gabrielle Harrison has to go to class,
As she runs for her bus pass.
With legs as long as a spider
And drinks cider.

Her smile is cute
Just like her lovely mother.
She has eyes
Just like her dad.

When the teacher turns around
She doesn't hear a sound.
She likes to have peace and quiet,
She is on a diet!

Hands as small as a mouse,
She lives in a posh house.
Hair like Cinderella,
Loves to play in the dark cellar.

Gabrielle Harrison (11)
St Edmund Arrowsmith RC High School, Wigan

MY SIMILE POEM

Thomas Foster comes to tech
With his great big ears and big long neck,
Everyone thinks it's a man-sized impostor,
When really it's only Thomas Foster.

His feet are big, his hands are too,
You couldn't shut his mouth with Superglue.
His clothes are smart and really cool,
But he tends to act the fool.

His dad is tall just like him,
His brother is a madman and can tear you limb from limb.
His mum is cool, she is the best,
She's better than all the rest.

He hates school, it's really bad,
Even though he's quite a clever lad.
In the corner bullies lurk,
Don't even mention homework.

Thomas Foster (12)
St Edmund Arrowsmith RC High School, Wigan

SIMON EGERTON

Simon Egerton comes to school,
Not looking like a fool.
Tries his best all the time
And doesn't step out of line.

My friends are fun,
We play in the sun.
We have some laughs
When we go to the swimming baths.

My family is smashing,
Everyone's always dashing
From place to place,
Always with a happy face.

School is for learning,
My brain is yearning
For information,
I need concentration.

Simon Egerton (11)
St Edmund Arrowsmith RC High School, Wigan

MY FAVOURITE THINGS

Birthdays, Christmas, Easter too,
Seeing elephants at the zoo.

Kentucky Fried Chicken and McDonald's chips,
Chocolate muffins, Doritos with dips.

Going to sleepovers with my friends,
Talking all night about the latest trends.

Cheese and pickle butties for my dinner,
My raffle ticket being a winner.

Golden beaches and a deep blue sea,
Going to a restaurant for my tea.

Being with my best friends and having a laugh,
Lying in a warm, relaxing bath.

But the thing that makes me happy the most
Is being tucked up in bed as warm as toast!

Jessica McKay (11)
St Edmund Arrowsmith RC High School, Wigan

FIRST DAY AT SCHOOL

The teachers were too nice,
The other children too loud,
The colour blue too overwhelming,
Thoughts rushed through my head,
Excited, yet curious,
But what am I doing here?
Learning - I was told.

The sound of chalk on the blackboard,
Shivered up my spine,
It got boring hearing people's pens clicking,
Many children cried,
I waited patiently for play time,
Although playing was fun
I feared the older kids,
The kids who might knock me down.

I remember well my first day at school.

Kate Houghton (11)
St Edmund Arrowsmith RC High School, Wigan

RACHEL BARTON

Rachel Barton comes to school
With eyes as blue as a swimming pool.
Her hair is blonde, her cheeks are red,
She sleeps like a log in her bed.

Rachel is a groovy gal
Who's everybody's mate.
She's funky and fantastic,
She's gorgeous and she's great.

Martin is her sporty brother,
Berni is her splendid mother,
Rebecca is her singing sis
Her mum's super boyfriend is Chris.

Rachel's friends Nicola and Georgie are quite small
But her friends Gem and Haliegh are really tall.
She has friends like Hannah, Nat and Leah,
They are great friends and that is clear.

Rachel Barton (11)
St Edmund Arrowsmith RC High School, Wigan

FIRST DAY AT SCHOOL

I saw a building all around,
Lots of kids banging their feet on the ground.
I felt scared and worried, no Mummy in sight,
I could hear loud children, so big in height.
Children crying, wanting to go home,
So did I, I was so alone.
No one would come near me,
It was as if they couldn't hear me.
I didn't like the selfish boys who took my toys away from me,
They started laughing, 'Hee, hee, hee.'
Then I realised how kind a teacher can be,
She told them off and they had to give them back to me.
My first day at primary school.

Briony McNelly (11)
St Edmund Arrowsmith RC High School, Wigan

FIRST DAY AT PRIMARY SCHOOL

Loads of little children screaming and shouting,
Mums and Dads talking,
Teachers blowing whistles to come inside,
Excited,
Scared,
Nervous,
Screaming,
Shouting,
Talking,
Seeing new children and seeing teachers,
Being by yourself at play time,
First day at primary school.

Sophie Oxenham (11)
St Edmund Arrowsmith RC High School, Wigan

FIRST DAY AT SCHOOL

Your mum drops you off at school,
But all you want to do is play pool.
You walk up to the big iron gates
And look inside and see your mates.
You quickly open the gates and run inside
And your mate shouts to you, 'My pet frog has died.'
The teacher comes out and blows her whistle
And her name is Miss Jistle.
We met our teacher, Mrs Bell,
But as she was talking a little boy fell.
He cut his knee
And the teacher said, 'I need a cup of tea.'
As the day flew by
I got hurt by a tie.
When home time came
The teacher hadn't learnt my name.

James Whyte (11)
St Edmund Arrowsmith RC High School, Wigan

MY FIRST DAY AT SCHOOL

Swarms of older children,
People rushing round,
Teachers call us in,
Nervous,
Anxious,
Children chatter,
Teachers can't get our attention,
Assembly's ended, scraping chairs,
Yes! Break time!

Jessica Woodward (12)
St Edmund Arrowsmith RC High School, Wigan

THOMAS SMITH

Thomas Smith comes to class,
With a head as square as a dinner pass.
As sly as a cat,
But as blind as a bat.

Thomas Smith comes to maths,
Thinking he is in Mass.
The teacher says, 'What's four times four?'
'You what! How am I meant to know.'

Thomas Smith comes to gym,
Looking very dim.
He climbed the rope,
Thinking he was the Pope.
So he thought someone would catch him
But no he landed on Tim.

Thomas Smith (12)
St Edmund Arrowsmith RC High School, Wigan

MONTHS OF THE YEAR

January brings the snow,
Makes our feet and fingers glow.
June brings roses,
Fills the children's hands with posies.
Dull November brings the blast
And then the leaves are whirling fast.
Then December brings the sleet,
Blazing fire and Christmas treat.

Claire Harvey (11)
St Edmund Arrowsmith RC High School, Wigan

MY SIMILE POEM

Jemma McGuigan comes to school
With eyes as blue as a swimming pool.
Ears like an elf's and teeth like rubbers
A good little girl is Jemma McGuiganers!

Jemma McGuigan goes outside
In the corner there she cries.
When her mates come up to her
They give her a nasty stare.

Jemma McGuigan's dad loves beer
And her mum loves to cheer.
All day long they have so much fun
Most of all and especially her mum!

Jemma McGuigan (11)
St Edmund Arrowsmith RC High School, Wigan

MY BROTHER SAM

My brother Sam is very naughty
He doesn't do what I say.
He runs about and screams and shouts
And is like this every day.

My brother Sam is very wild
He's like a kangaroo.
He always likes to jump on me
And on the furniture too.

Jake Almond (11)
St Edmund Arrowsmith RC High School, Wigan

LIAM HALL

Liam comes to school like a right fool
And has eyes as brown as a chocolate pool
His hair is trimmed and cool.

He runs very fast
And he knows it won't last.
He's soon out of puff
He's had enough.

I have a dog he is called Jasper
I have a brother he scares me like Casper.
I have a dad he's not that bad
I have a mum she's number one.
I have a sister
She's never in but I don't miss her.

Liam Hall (11)
St Edmund Arrowsmith RC High School, Wigan

THE MANTA RAY

Very big but very flat
At the bottom of the sea
Try and see this camouflaged creature

Very big but very flat
Long and wide
It tries to hide.

Very big but very flat
Loves the bottom of the sea
Small creatures fear

The manta ray.

David Cooper (13)
St Edmund Arrowsmith RC High School, Wigan

FIRST DAY AT SCHOOL

Classroom so big it echoes around me,
Kids crying surround me.
So many big people crowd me.

Scared and worried.

Older children talking loudly,
Outside traffic grounds me,
Cries of waiting for mums.

Play time, such a joyful time.
Leaving Mum at the start of school
Feels like leaving home.

First day at school.

Adam Jones (11)
St Edmund Arrowsmith RC High School, Wigan

SEAN WALSH

Sean Walsh comes to class
Running for his dinner pass.
Late as usual, in a mess,
A boy with a lot on his chest
But very sharp in his test.
He can be a pest at times
He climbs trees and sometimes gets told off.
He can be a pest,
He can do well in a test.
He sometimes goes on a quest.
He can be silly,
He can be good.
He has pudding after tea.

Sean Walsh (11)
St Edmund Arrowsmith RC High School, Wigan

MICHAEL LEONARD

Michael Leonard comes to school,
Looking like a fool,
His hair is cool
Like a swimming pool.
Standing on a stool
Is Michael Leonard the fool.

My family can make me glad,
And sometimes they make me sad.
But mostly they appeal
And make a really good deal.

My sister is a pain
And mostly insane.
But really she is good
Although she likes to play in the mud.

Then I come to Dad and Mum
Now we are nearly done.
They look after my sister and me
Every day they make our tea.

Michael Leonard (11)
St Edmund Arrowsmith RC High School, Wigan

THE KING OF THE JUNGLE

He prowls around with his pride,
He likes his food wet or dried.
In the animal bungle
He's the king of the jungle,
For here's the lion,
We've got to hide.

Jodie Garner (11)
St Edmund Arrowsmith RC High School, Wigan

LAURA KAVANEY

Laura Kavaney comes to school
With eyes as blue as a swimming pool.
Her hair's light brown, her cheeks are rosy
She loves her bed it's soft and cosy.

Laura Kavaney's in the playground
She always has her friends around.
They make her laugh, they make her smile,
She has them round for tea once in a while.

Laura Kavaney's in PE,
She's as busy as a bee.
She is happy,
She always smiles
She hopes she doesn't have to run a hundred miles.

Laura Kavaney's going home
On the bus, all alone.
She loves her family very much
Because they have a gentle touch.

Laura Kavaney (11)
St Edmund Arrowsmith RC High School, Wigan

MY PET DOG

My pet dog has a ball,
He runs to me when I call.
When I am lonely or when I am sad
He gives me a cuddle and makes me glad.
I love him from here to a million miles away
And he's going nowhere cos he's here to stay.

Samantha Singleton (11)
St Edmund Arrowsmith RC High School, Wigan

KATHARINE CHRISTOPHER

Katharine Christopher comes to class,
With eyes that sparkle like clear glass.
Her hair is blonde, her teeth are white,
It all adds up to her face being bright.

Katharine Christopher is really nice,
You could say she is as cool as ice.
She is really, really clever,
But never boring, no not ever.

Herself and her family are very caring,
Their top two things are being nice and sharing.
Her family consists of her mum and dad,
Katharine and Nathan, a typical lad.

Now we're up to her best friend,
Sophie Taylor, they could chat and never end.
She has loads and loads of other mates,
Who think of her as really great!

Katharine Christopher (11)
St Edmund Arrowsmith RC High School, Wigan

HAYLEIGH CROSS

Hayleigh Cross comes to school
With eyes as wide as a swimming pool.
Her appearance is smart
And she likes to take part.

Hayleigh is cool
She is in no way a fool.
She is always happy
And she is never snappy.

We are a family of four
My mum, my dad, my sister for sure.
There is a cat on the mat
And that is that!

My friends are the best
They put me to the test.
They are a great bunch of guys
And they are funny but wise.

Hayleigh Cross (12)
St Edmund Arrowsmith RC High School, Wigan

NICOLA SIMPSON

Nicola Simpson comes to school
With hair as long as a swimming pool,
With eyes as wide as the sea
You've never seen anyone like me!

She's got a good sense of humour
She always starts a good rumour!
She's louder than a swarm of bees
Which is heard over the seas.

Her dad is called Tony
He isn't very bony!
Then there's her sister
Who always has a blister.

Friends, she's got loads of them
She can't remember half of them!
It's like she's in a wasp's nest
But Rachel, Hayleigh and Leah are the best!

Nicola Simpson
St Edmund Arrowsmith RC High School, Wigan

REBECCA LYON!

Rebecca Lyon comes to school
Looking like a silly fool.
Eyes wide open, a muddy brown
On her face there is a frown.

As cheeky as a monkey,
Looking really funky.
As loud as a gorilla when it's mad,
Only at school she's ever sad.

My brothers stay in bed all day,
While my dad's working far away.
My mum's a prison officer, she's very busy
All the cons drive her dizzy.

My friends are at school, thinking the same as me,
Why are we here? It's as boring as can be.
So when it's home time, we all have fun,
Cos our day at school is over and done!

Rebecca Lyon (11)
St Edmund Arrowsmith RC High School, Wigan

DANIEL PODESTA

Daniel Podesta comes down the streets
Whistling to everyone he meets
He is really strange,
I wish he could change.

Daniel is dark,
As dark as night.
He's quite well-built,
Someone you wouldn't want to fight.

He lives with his mum,
She can be quite good fun.
She drives him to school,
She acts really cool.

His mates are the best,
Better than all the rest.
Come rain or shine,
Together these boys you will find.

Daniel Podesta (11)
St Edmund Arrowsmith RC High School, Wigan

LEAH ROBERTS

Leah Roberts comes to school,
With eyes as blue as an icy pool.
Hair like the fur of a small brown mouse,
Hiding away inside the house.

She's as chirpy as a bird,
As warm as the sun.
She gets picked in class,
(She's always the one).

Her dad works from dawn to dusk,
Her mum hoovers, washes and dusts
And her sister drives her completely nuts.
With all her moods, ifs and buts.

She's got loads of friends,
Some drive her round the bend.
But the ones that stand above the rest
Are Nicola, Rachel, Emma and Rebecca - the best!

Leah Roberts (11)
St Edmund Arrowsmith RC High School, Wigan

SOPHIE TAYLOR

Sophie Taylor comes to school,
looking really, really cool!
With eyes as green,
as you've ever seen!

She's as chirpy as a bird,
she shows she's happy without a word!
Like the sun she's warm and bright,
although she thinks she's always right.

She eats like a mouse,
and loves her house!
Runs almost like a cheetah,
everyone wants to meet her!

Mum's real clean,
Dad's garden is pristine!
Now Sophie's in the park,
playing, chatting, happy as a lark.

Sophie Taylor (11)
St Edmund Arrowsmith RC High School, Wigan

TODD

Todd Fishwick comes to school
With eyes as small as a bead.
With hair like coal and teeth like dough
He makes fun of the old fo'.

As he walked to school
He stood in a muddy pool
The other kids laugh, taunt and tease
About his muddy knees.

As he got home
He tripped on a stone.
Stumbling into the house, his mother was in bed
His father was at work
His auntie Patricia was a real jerk.

He has no friends
He has no dough
He is really, really poor.

Todd Fishwick (11)
St Edmund Arrowsmith RC High School, Wigan

MARTIN EGERTON

Martin Egerton comes to school,
With hair as brown as a muddy pool.
When he comes looking very tall,
With eyes as round as a football.

I like to laugh, I don't like to cry,
My friends are good and so am I.
Sometimes I'm happy, sometimes I'm sad.
I'm not always bad.

My mum is good, my dad is smart,
I'm not that good at art.
My brother and sister get along very well
And so do I, as well.

My friends are kind,
They don't lie and don't mind.
Sometimes they make me sad,
But when we make up we are glad.

Martin Egerton (11)
St Edmund Arrowsmith RC High School, Wigan

MY SIMILE POEM - LEWIS

Lewis North catches the bus,
His hair is brown, as brown as rust.
A spot under his nose, it's always seen,
Some people pick on him because they are mean.

His friends say he is funny you will see,
If you listen to his jokes with me.
He normally makes his friends smile,
Longer than a little while.

His mum is kind and so is his dad,
But not his step dad he is just mad.
He has to put up with him every day,
This is his life and it has to be this way.

He has quite a lot of mates,
None of them like Gareth Gates.
The best one at football,
Has got to be his good mate Paul.

Lewis North (11)
St Edmund Arrowsmith RC High School, Wigan

MY SIMILE POEM

Gemma Withington runs into class,
But she trips over and breaks some glass!
Her teacher stands there with a frown on his face,
And says to Gemma, 'You are a disgrace!'

Hair as brown as a puddle of mud,
She walks around with a thud, thud, thud.
She's as chirpy as a little bird,
When Gemma talks no one can ever say a word!

Her mum sighs and drinks cups of tea,
While her dad looks at her school trip fee.
Her brother is always skating down a slope,
How does Gemma Withington ever cope?

She's as sly as a cat,
As quick as a bat.
She always wants to be number one,
She's quite a girl that Gemma Withington.

Gemma Withington (11)
St Edmund Arrowsmith RC High School, Wigan

LUKE PIETRASZKO

Luke Pietraszko goes to football,
With specs the size of two golf balls.
Hair light brown and teeth like metal
He always loves to boil the kettle.

Luke Pietraszko comes to class,
Running for his dinner pass.
Working hard all day long,
Always trying to get along.

Luke Pietraszko has some friends,
Who will always remain the best of friends.
They always laugh with one another
And always play sport together.

Luke Pietraszko has a family
Who always love to eat candy.
Mum is rushing all the time,
My autistic brother is playing all the time.

Luke Pietraszko (12)
St Edmund Arrowsmith RC High School, Wigan

ANDREW HIGGINS

Andrew rides to school like a king,
He tries not to worry about anything.
He dreams of doing all his maths,
And then he doesn't get the teacher's wrath.

His hair is blonde, uniform smart,
He comes to school to play a part.
His athletic build is very strong,
As he tries to stay all day long.

He's as sharp as a knife,
As he takes all things in life.
He always has his nose in a book
And Andrew loves to cook.

For his hobby Andrew loves to putt the shot,
Gold, silver and bronze are the trophies he's got.
He also loves to do the high jump,
Until he comes down with a bump.

Andrew Higgins (11)
St Edmund Arrowsmith RC High School, Wigan

TIM HALLIDAY

Tim Halliday comes to class,
Being late he runs down the path.
He plonks down like a ten ton weight
The school he does not appreciate.

His homework is never in,
The merit prize he'll never win.
Bored, dreamland is his home
As he sits in the corner of his dome.

At home there are four
He couldn't put up with any more.
Tim lives in a house near school
And has a hole in the garden for a swimming pool.

He hates 8.40
So he is very naughty.
Now the rest of the day
Quickly flies away.

Tim Halliday (11)
St Edmund Arrowsmith RC High School, Wigan

ZOE JACKSON

Zoe Jackson comes to school
All her friends think she's dead cool.
Late for class she'll never be
Sounds a nice girl, she does to me.

All her family simply adore her,
And if she's hated she won't care.
With great long legs she'll run a mile
And cheer up anybody with her smile.

She looks dead cool with all her friends,
When spending time with her the fun never ends.
With her stylish clothes and good attitude,
She'll always be in a very good mood.

She lives in a house with her mum and dad
And a dog called Della who's barking mad.
Her sister's name is Emma, she is very clever
Although she'll never tell her, she loves her to bits.

Zoe Jackson (11)
St Edmund Arrowsmith RC High School, Wigan

GRAEME HOLDEN

Graeme Holden comes to school,
thinking he is very cool.
He thinks that he's hard
and he's really as strong as a dart.

His best friend is Martin Cunnliffe,
who got hit with a bin lid.
They both want to be actors,
but their second choice is driving tractors.

In his family he has two brothers and two sisters,
and of course his mum and dad,
sometimes they can be bad
but then again they're all quite nice.

His house is full of creepy-crawlies
but every one has died.
Thanks to Graeme,
but everyone has to pay him.

Graeme Holden (11)
St Edmund Arrowsmith RC High School, Wigan

I LOVE SUMMER!

I love summer because . . .
I love the smell of freshly cut grass,
and barbecues as you pass.
I love that dark tan from the sun
and watching kids on the streets having fun.
I love having water fights,
and I love those long summer nights.
I love going on holiday and relaxing in the sun,
I love having fun!

Lauren Patton (14)
St Gabriel's RC High School, Bury

THE GHOSTS AND MONSTERS

There's a bump in the night,
Which causes quite a fright
And Jimmy to wake in his bed.
All the ghosts and monsters in his room,
Or may be they're just in his head.

No. They're all parading round his room,
The monsters, the ghosts and the ghouls.

Jimmy grabs a flashlight,
To aim into the dark night,
At all the spooks.
They each disappear one by one,
Taking with them all their *boos!*

So, now Jimmy can rest peacefully
And safely in his head, too,
Until he's dozing off to sleep, when . . .
Wooo!

Tom McMahon (12)
St Gabriel's RC High School, Bury

THE EARTH

The Earth moves like the wind in a gentle breeze,
Like a snail slithering along the floor,
Like a snake following its prey slowly,
Like a bird gliding through the air,
Like a leaf gently drifting down from the tree,
Like a flower growing from the seed,
Like a fish flowing through the water in the sea,
But the Earth is a beautiful place to be
So let's keep it that way.

Daryl Myers (12)
St Gabriel's RC High School, Bury

FOOTBALL - ONE GREAT GAME!

Kick off at ten, ready again,
Number 16, same as Roy Keane,
Rarin' to go, put my skills on show,
Will today be the day, when I put it away?
Top corner; bottom, placed or a pen?
Adrenaline rush, was that a push?
The ref did not see, what was meant to be.
Ball passed to me, the goal I can see,
Scissors, Matthews; passed to Caz,
Over to Trace, who's really got pace;
Whipped in the net, not the last I'll bet.
Free kick to them, straight to our number 10,
She flies down the wing, and puts in a swing,
Onto my head, 16 in red.
I bring it to feet and volley - so sweet!
We're on a roll, what a beautiful goal!
My heart's beatin' fast, want this to last!
The pride and the glory, I tell in my story.
A part of this team, I'm living my dream,
A chance for so few, a place with Man U.

Melanie Willan (14)
St Gabriel's RC High School, Bury

GIRL FROM BURY

There was a young girl from Bury
Who left the shops in a hurry
Her knickers fell down
In the middle of town
And her face was as red as a cherry.

Danielle Knight (12)
St Gabriel's RC High School, Bury

I HAVE A GOAT WITH LONG PIGTAILS

I have a goat with long pigtails
I have a girl with fluffy skin
I have a rabbit with buttons
I have a jacket with brown spots
I have a giraffe with woolly ears
I have a sheep with a big nose
I have a pig with loud screams
I have a sister with long floppy ears
I have an elf with long legs
I have an elephant with pink fussy hair
I have a clown with small feet
I have a baby with long arms
I have a Mr Streach with a pink rabbit's tail
I have a cartoon with no spine
I have a slug with a fancy cover
I have a book with green teeth
I have an old lady with bright yellow hair
I have a dolphin with gold stripes
I have a skirt with lots of words
I have a story with a balloon
I have a child without a doubt
I have the answer to this riddle.

Amy Hall (12)
St Gabriel's RC High School, Bury

SLOWLY

Slowly Alfie walks to his tray
Slowly Alfie gets on his way
Slowly Alfie gets there
Slowly Alfie lets me stroke his fur.

Samantha Bowker (12)
St Gabriel's RC High School, Bury

MY WEDDING

It was like a fairy tale, my fairy tale,
My wonderful white wedding,
Held in a field filled with buttercups,
My family to the left, as I walked down the aisle,
The sun shining above us,
I could see the one I loved.
It all seemed too perfect and of course it was,
The next step I took was the last one that day,
I fell and banged my head,
The bang was like thunder,
Everybody heard and rushed over,
I was taken away in an ambulance
And that was it,
The end of my fairy tale, it was now a nightmare.

Siobhán Murphy (14)
St Gabriel's RC High School, Bury

WATCH OUT!

I'm fourteen now and nice to know
Time moves fast but hold on *woah!*
What happened to that little tree
It almost grew as fast as me
The fantastic computer game
Look at it now pathetic, lame
I now feel all around me
Everything's changing, new things I see
I travel to far off places
Visit cities and meet new faces
The past fourteen years have been great fun
But look behind you here I come!

Charlotte Miller (14)
St Gabriel's RC High School, Bury

116

CHRISTMAS DINNER

The turkey aroma fills the air,
It has been prepared with the utmost care.
Carrots, broccoli, sprouts and more,
It's what the biggest plates are for.
Country stuffing full of herbs,
Even the largest appetite curbs.
Roast potatoes, crispy and brown,
Mum has really gone to town.
Gallons of gravy and cranberry sauce,
It's enough to fill a horse.
Christmas pudding with holly ablaze,
Must not forget our traditional ways.
A mountain of washing up straight after lunch,
But it's worth it after all we've had to munch.

Rebecca Proctor (13)
St Gabriel's RC High School, Bury

GONE FISHING

I told my mum I'd gone fishing.
She shouted back, 'Keep wishing!'
An hour later my bite alarm rang,
My line went tight with a twang.
I thought a carp, with its fight,
Fortunately for me I was right.
Twenty minutes to get it in,
I thought it was amazin'.
My mate took the photo,
16 pounds all together in total.
Then I returned it to the water,
Ha! My mum that taught her.

Alec Roughley (14)
St Gabriel's RC High School, Bury

THE OBSERVANT MOON

A stubble of golden, yellow corn
Swept a vast area with a glow
That competed against the stars.
Crumbs of shadow fell across the cobbled
Plain as if something was feeding off it.
Is it a horse or those rats?
Maybe it's the evil creatures of the night
Trying to take over the world.
'Eh, who's that figure yonder?'
'Thou art a poet, plain and simple as can be.'
'What are you doing?'

'I am writing about an observant moon.'

Daniel Cassidy (14)
St Gabriel's RC High School, Bury

THE SCHOOL BUS

Each morning at 8.30 I get on the 474,
I really wish I hadn't got to do it anymore,
The driver is so grumpy,
The passengers are as well,

All the different people have a different story to tell,
The ladies are all rushing,
The men who hate their work,
The kids who really wish a school day they could shirk,

And then there's me, a little passenger seated on this trip,
Wishing I could go back home and have a longer kip!

Faith Collinge (13)
St Gabriel's RC High School, Bury

BLUE!

Blue is the colour of my eyes,
The colour of the seas,
The colour of the skies!

Blue is the colour of sadness,
The colour of slow music,
Not the colour of madness!

Blue is a colour in green,
A colour to be seen,
The colour of a dream!

Blue is the colour of this ink,
The colour of my pen,
The water in a sink!

Blue is the Earth with no land,
The blood inside my hand,
Of Pluto on which we will land!

Blue is the colour of my eyes.

Michael Molloy (13)
St Gabriel's RC High School, Bury

THE SUN

The sun is bright
It spreads the light
All around the world
And when the moon comes
Rising up into the sky
The sun goes to bed
For another night.

Grace Adams (13)
St Gabriel's RC High School, Bury

Birds In The Sky

The birds in the sky are flying up high!
The trees down below are waving to and fro!

The people in their houses
Are looking at their blouses!

Their dogs are saying pardon
While messing up the garden!

The girls are at school
While the boys are playing pool!

I am getting tired now
So I'm going to stop now!

Rebecca Roberts (11)
St Gabriel's RC High School, Bury

Thy Angel

Thy angel of light prepares to leap into flight
Protected me now and protected me then
If only I could change what I did then.

I hope for you
I hope for me
I hope for all eternity.

Life and death should be treated well
Our life gives us opportunities
But death we do not know too well.

James Raynard (12)
St Gabriel's RC High School, Bury

CREATION

There's beauty in a cobweb as it's filled with a raindrop
There's beauty in an egg just about to pop.

There's beauty in every freckle on everyone's face
There's beauty in any human, black, white or any race.

There's beauty in a person who laughs and smiles for joy
There's beauty in every person, old or young; girl or boy.

There's beauty in every scale as it's placed by God on a fish
There's beauty in every ingredient put in a single dish.

There's beauty in every stem of grass full of its healthy green
There's beauty in everything I've told you and everything I've seen.

Raisa Richardson (12)
St Gabriel's RC High School, Bury

AUTUMN LEAVES

Autumn leaves falling down,
falling down to the ground.

Autumn leaves brown and crisp,
crackling and crunching under your feet.

Autumn leaves whirling around,
whirling around to the ground.

Autumn leaves cover the floor,
wherever you go they still cover the floor.

Autumn leaves disappear,
the months grow colder and now the snow is here!

Amy Cosgrove (14)
St Gabriel's RC High School, Bury

MUHAMMED ALI

Muhammed, Muhammed Ali,
He floats like a butterfly,
He stings like a bee,
He swings with his left,
He swings with his right,
His opponent will come down,
On the count of three,
He can't be defeated,
He can't fall down,
He will always have the crown,
He swings with his left,
He swings with his right,
Look at the boy he's carrying the fight,
He knocks his opponent,
Out of the ring,
The ref wears a frown,
He can't start counting,
Till Joe Frazer falls down!

Daniel Horwood (12)
St Gabriel's RC High School, Bury

ANIMALS

A   nimals are all different!
N   ight-time is when some animals come out.
I   nsects creep and crawl everywhere.
M   onkeys are mysterious and mischievous.
A   nts are small and tiny.
L   ions roar and rage.
S   nakes are slimy and slithering.

Jonathan Mayall (11)
St Gabriel's RC High School, Bury

PARENTS

Be back in at eight,
Don't you dare be late,
Don't talk to me like that,
Don't you give me backchat,
What time do you call this?
Don't you give me that twist,
Go upstairs and tidy your room
Drop the act of doom and gloom,
Don't you dare be moody with me,
Go and make me a cup of tea,
This teenage thing is all too much,
You look at me like I speak Dutch,
Being a parent is very hard,
(But putting up with them is harder!)

Caroline Jane Dunne (13)
St Gabriel's RC High School, Bury

AMBER'S POEM

A   mber is my name
M   illie is the name of my cat
B   ury is the place I live
E   ating ice cream is best
R   ed roses are beautiful

K   eys of success
E   njoy shopping with my mates
O   r sometimes we go to the cinema
W   hen we do go to the cinema we buy lots of sweets
N   ever trust boys.

Amber Keown (12)
St Gabriel's RC High School, Bury

WHAT AM I?

Every time you're feeling sad
I'm like your own little pad.
To write your feelings down on me
Is as easy as can be.
I will keep them locked away
Ready to use every day.
You can write what you want
In whatever type of font.
You can write how you feel,
What you had for a meal.
Who you fancy,
Who you don't,
You can write your secrets out,
So you don't have to shout.
Can you guess what I am?
I'm a diary,
Yes I am!

Kerry Smith (12)
St Gabriel's RC High School, Bury

THE SKY

The sun is hot,
It lights the day.
The moon is not,
It fades away.
The stars glisten,
If you listen
And the birds tweet,
In the heat
Of another day.

Mark Hudson (11)
St Gabriel's RC High School, Bury

Parents' Favourite Sayings

No you can't have a parrot.
Another detention!
No you already have one, go on then.
Go to your bedroom.
You have to buy it with your own money.
Do your bed.
No more animals.
Stop watching the telly.
Do your homework.
Take your shoes off.
You pay the phone bill.
While you're under my roof you'll obey my rules.
Take the dog for a walk.
You're grounded.
(But these are only saying so as long as I'm a child
I'll never take any notice of them.)

Luke Powell (12)
St Gabriel's RC High School, Bury

Mum's New Car

It's red and shiny and has nice new wheels
Clunk click our seat belts are on
Mum turns the keys
Vroom vroom goes the engine
Oh no says me
Like a white knuckle ride my hands clutched to my seat
Oh no says me
We set off and go
Before long we are at home at last
I sigh with relief
But oh no there's tomorrow.

Matthew Sherratt (12)
St Gabriel's RC High School, Bury

COLOURS OF THE RAINBOW WE FIND AROUND SCHOOL

Red is sometimes the colour of the board marker
The teacher uses to write with.
Orange is the colour of the chairs we sit on
And work on in class.
Yellow is the colour of the cupboards we use for storage.
Green is the colour of the shirt the teacher sometimes wears
To come to school in.
Blue is the colour of the desks we use to work in.
Indigo is the colour of people's hair bobbles
To keep their hair tied back.
Violet is the colour of the scarf the teacher wraps
Around her neck to keep her warm.

Kelly Donovan (12)
St Gabriel's RC High School, Bury

A DAY IN THE LIFE OF A BEE

I wish I could fly like a bee.
Imagine all the wonderful things I see.
Children playing in the town,
Hopscotch written on the ground.
Music bellowing through the streets,
People together tapping their feet.
Laughter filling everyone's hearts,
They were all so happy from the start,
No one worrying about a thing.
Everyone listens to Mary sing,
Holding hands and eyes closed,
So many people close to home.
Imagine all the wonderful things I see
If I could fly just like a bee.

Ellen Greene (12)
St Gabriel's RC High School, Bury

FRIENDS

I have a friend who is small
I have a friend who is tall.
One of my friends has a silly face
One of my friends is of a different race.
My best friend is Jamie-Leigh
My best friend is the best there can be.
Two of my friends love to dance
Two of my friends live in France.
I have friends, some which are boys
I have friends that make loads of noise.
Most of my friends are disco divas
Most of my friends aren't quitters but achievers.
One of my friends is a champion runner
One of my friends can draw, paint and colour.
But, I did once have a friend who I wanted to be
I did once have a friend who was special to me.

Emma Testa (13)
St Gabriel's RC High School, Bury

SEPTEMBER 11TH

The World Trade Centers are falling
As the firemen are calling,
People are crying,
Their loved ones dying,
People are jumping,
The firemen pumping,
They rush to the scene,
Maybe they were over-keen,
Thousands have died,
Their loved ones cried.

Richard Brackley (13)
St Gabriel's RC High School, Bury

Poem

Roses are red,
Violets are blue,
I love you,
Do you love me too?

Skies are blue,
Nights are black,
I love you and that's a fact.

When time takes its toll,
I dance round a pole,
I'll keep you happy,
More than a wet nappy.

You took my heart right from the start,
I'll never regret even though it was a bet,
You sent my heart away, I felt well spent,
You slither through my fingers like a serpent.

It's funny you know,
That I do love you so,
I shall never ever let you go again.

Kirstie Hambleton (11)
St Gabriel's RC High School, Bury

BMX-ing

BMX-ing is a competitive sport
My favourite riders are Dave Mirra and Zack Shaw
They pull amazing tricks I have never seen before
Like bar spins, flairs and much, much more

Competitions are held near and far
Get there by bike, coach or even car
Watch people set up their bikes, pedals, wheels and bars
Maybe BMX-ing is played on Mars

Comps are either street, vert or dirt
Wear their protection pads under their shirt
If they don't they will get hurt
Like good old dirty old Bert.

Sam Kay (13)
St Gabriel's RC High School, Bury

THE SOLDIERS' LAMENT

Upon a hill I stood in wait,
When there I saw come trudging past,
Four men with packs upon their backs.

Their clothes were torn,
Their faces worn,
But still they marched on and on.

The leader turned and managed a smile,
'Come on lads, just one more mile.'

With heavy hearts they struggled on by,
I heard each uttering a mournful sigh.
Then I heard gunshots upon the wind.

They didn't turn,
Even once,
But as the bullets hit their backs,
They disappeared into the air.

I ran to the spot, on which they had stood
And found nought . . .
But poppies.

Jessica Stott (12)
St Gabriel's RC High School, Bury

MY GARDEN

I really hate my garden,
It gets me every time,
From rose bushes to stones,
No matter what I do,
It gets me every time!

I really hate that rose bush,
It gets me every time,
I come to water it, ow!
It gets me every time!

I really hate that fountain,
It gets me every time,
I come to switch it on,
And slip in the water on the floor,
It gets me every time!

I really hate that doorstep,
It gets me every time,
I either trip or slip on it,
It gets me every time!

I really hate those stones,
They get me every time,
I water plants barefoot,
Ow! They spiked me,
They get me every time!

I really hate my garden,
It gets me every time,
Now I do not dare
To step into my garden!

David Cockcroft (11)
St Gabriel's RC High School, Bury

EXCUSES

I'm sorry Mum, you didn't say
I had to make my bed today,
I'm sorry Sir, I wasn't there
When you said to write a prayer,
I'm sorry Miss, I had the flu
I didn't know what I had to do,
I'm sorry Dad, I know you're mad
But when it broke I too felt sad.

I'm sorry Mum, I thought you said
Not to wash up, you'd do it instead,
I'm sorry Sir, please understand
My French is weak, I'm from England,
I'm sorry Miss, I could not see
The board was too far away from me,
I'm sorry Dad, I misunderstood
I thought you said to drop the wood.

I'm sorry Mum, it's my mistake
I thought you said to eat the cake,
I'm sorry Miss, I thought you meant
The class was over so I went,
I'm sorry Sir, I missed PE
I trapped my finger and hurt my knee,
I'm sorry Dad, I didn't start the riot
It was Mum and her ongoing diet.
I'm sorry, I'm sorry, I'm sorry, you see!
Excuses just come so easy to me!

Maria Dillon (12)
St Gabriel's RC High School, Bury

WHAT WOULD LIFE BE?

What would life be without a song,
The chorus of birds at the break of dawn,
The rhythm of crickets to the jungle beat,
Flowers dancing in the summer heat?

What would life be without any light,
No sign of hope ever shining bright,
A world of darkness every day,
No sun to shine its every ray?

What would life be, all alone,
A tiny place, left on your own,
A deserted world, not a body around,
Searching near and far, no soul ever found?

But what would life be without a fight,
A world of peace, a divine right,
No more crying, no more pain,
Tortured families from this awful game?

Think about what this life would be,
A better place, oh how I long to see.

Laura Chesterfield (14)
St Gabriel's RC High School, Bury

HELLO, GOODBYE

Hello holidays, goodbye school.
Hello sweets, goodbye teeth.
Hello summer, goodbye winter.
Hello sun, goodbye rain.
Hello friends, goodbye loneliness.

Kelsey Connor (12)
St Gabriel's RC High School, Bury

ALL THE SEASONS

Spring is good,
Spring is fine,
Mum likes drinking blackberry wine.

All the trees blossom out,
All the flowers pop and sprout,
While I lie down catching a tan,
My dad is cooling with a fan.

While it starts to cool down,
I begin to give a frown,
All the leaves leave their trees,
While my grandma and grandad sit by the sea.

It is now Christmas,
Parents in bed,
Children downstairs waiting to be fed,
I heard Father Christmas was in town,
So I got up and lost my frown.
I waited and waited for him to come,
Then when he did my presents weighed a tonne!

Katherine Mason (13)
St Gabriel's RC High School, Bury

THE DOBERMAN

Strong, bold and fearless he looks, patrolling the garden,
searching for cats,
sniffing the bushes, looking under fences.
No cats anywhere, are they asleep or are they too scared to come in?
He lies down to sleep, one eye open, you can never be too sure
if they'll try to come in.

Jan Skrzypczak (11)
St Gabriel's RC High School, Bury

SPORTS

There are many sports.
Some are fun,
That is if you like to run.
Many are played in the sun,
Cricket never in the rain,
Which sometimes can be a pain.
Football is a popular sport,
Good for both rich and poor,
But it often leaves you quite sore.
It always leaves you wanting more.
Basketball is also popular,
It is simple to play,
You can do it any day,
So go and play!

Edward Scott (13)
St Gabriel's RC High School, Bury

I'M LATE

I'm late, I'm late
I'm going out the gate.
The bus is near,
It's almost here.
I'm on the bus,
Me and Gus.
The bus is late,
For me and my mate.
It's five past nine
And still street signs.
We're here
And we both deserve a beer.

Mark Fitzpatrick (13)
St Gabriel's RC High School, Bury

HORROR FILM!

The audience sits,
Their eyes transfixed,
Surprise! - The killer's revealed!
Some scream, others squeal,
The popcorn flies up in the air,
I slide deep down into my chair
While the killer's temper starts to flare
And the helpless victim flees upstairs.
She hides, then waits
For the usual fate.
Everyone gasps,
As the killer grasps
The handle of the door . . .
. . . suspense; horror; blood; gore . . .
The body listless on the floor!

Maria Richardson (14)
St Gabriel's RC High School, Bury

MY LITTLE SISTER

My little sister is so annoying,
My little sister is always moaning.
My little sister wets the bed,
My little sister banged her head.
My little sister is always crying,
My little sister is always lying.
My little sister loves TV,
My little sister is not sure about me,
And the worst habit she has and knows,
My little sister picks her nose.

Maria Hunt (11)
St Gabriel's RC High School, Bury

SUNRISE!

As the golden sphere rises up above the land,
The light shimmers across the soft sand,
The air smells fresh and new.
In the early parts of the morning you can see dew,
The calm blue sea glistens and swiftly moves back
and forth and side to side.
It leaves all sorts of creatures as out goes the tide,
As it gets to 7 o'clock early birds start to appear,
Their beautiful song brings to my eye a tear.
Shop owners, postmen and souvenir stall keepers start
their work
Whilst early morning tourists watch them and smirk.
The surfers grab their boards and hit the waves
When the restless holidaymakers lie down and sunbathe.
Day has broken and at the moment the sun is tame
But who knows how the day will go in sunny *Spain.*

Tara Berry (13)
St Gabriel's RC High School, Bury

FOOTBALL WITH MAN CITY

I like football, it's the best,
It's better than all the rest.
When I watch Man City play,
It's like relaxing at the end of the day.
A yellow card it's all the same,
It's only the ref you have to blame.
At the end of the match when Man City have won,
Everyone applauds for the good job they have done.
When I walk to the car there is lots of applause,
Then my dad and I set off home to find out the rest of the scores.

Robert Kavanagh (11)
St Gabriel's RC High School, Bury

MY FAMILY

My family are all cute teddy bears,
Waiting to be cuddled.

They are bright blues,
Cheering up my life.

They are cuddly tigers,
Cute but strong.

They are hot suns,
Gleaming down on me.

They are golden apples,
Ripe and strong.

They are happy thoughts,
Giving me that warm feeling.

Most of all they're my family.
Giving me all of their love.

Katy Howcroft (11)
St Gabriel's RC High School, Bury

MY BEDROOM

My bedroom is pink and purple combined
It's always a tip, but I don't mind
The girl on the wall looks oh so cool
If I dressed like that I'd look like a fool

I did it these colours to keep out my brother
CD or TV, it's one or the other
I storm in my room when my mum gives me stick
And transform myself into one *groovy chick.*

Rebecca Tough (11)
St Gabriel's RC High School, Bury

THE STORM

The crash of thunder,
A flash of light,
The scream of the wind,
It sounds like a fight.

The trees sway and creak,
The rain beats down,
Some storms are scary,
And exceptionally loud.

It thunders again,
The lightning strikes,
You gaze in awe,
Wow, what a sight!

Sara Haniak (14)
St Gabriel's RC High School, Bury

MATCH DAY

I walk into the floodlit ground,
To meet with a wall of very loud sound.
The atmosphere is really great,
I find my seat and can hardly wait.
The players come out of the tunnel,
The fans begin to roar,
Oh no! Blackburn are the first ones to score.
We finally get a chance on goal
And City are drawing 'cause they put it through the hole.
So the game has finished as a draw,
Let's hope next game they'll go one more!

Claire Dorey (11)
St Gabriel's RC High School, Bury

ONE DARK NIGHT

Trees scratched me with arthritic branches,
As I neared the dilapidated house.
In the window I saw a sad, frail face
And in a shrivelled hand, a small black mouse.
I turned to look to the gloomy forest
And wondered if I should go back.
I looked at the house a second time
And noticed a small, narrow track.
I ran as fast as a panther up the path
That led to the old, rotten door.
It was the face again, with a sharp, bloody knife,
I knew I could write no more!

Anna Roberts (11)
St Gabriel's RC High School, Bury

SCHOOL

School's alright I suppose,
But sometimes I would rather doze.
Sometimes it gets really boring,
Other days the day goes soaring.
I like to play with my friends,
I hope that lunch will never end.
Sometimes when I lie in bed,
I think of what lies ahead.
The dinners are so really great,
I cannot wait till the school fete.
I can't wait until we cook,
For English we need to read a book.

Joseph Bodell (11)
St Gabriel's RC High School, Bury

WALKING . . .

I have walked metres, I have walked miles,
Over rotting logs and past dusty stiles.
I have walked here and I have walked there:
In fact, I have walked almost everywhere.
I have walked up, I have walked down,
I have walked all around this town.
I have walked low, I have walked high
I am still breathless, without a sigh.
I have walked on the land and in the sea.
Still no one will walk with me.
I have walked over hills and in the waves
Past old country cottages and cold, dark caves.
Still no one walks with me,
Walking and walking endlessly,
Walking . . .
Walking . . .
Walking . . .

Liam Roberts (15)
St Gabriel's RC High School, Bury

I LIKE THE SOUND OF . . .

I like the sound of holidays today,
I like the sound that we're going away.
I like the sound that it's going to be sunny,
I like the sound of 'Have more money.'
I like the sound of no more school,
I like the sound that there's no rule.
I like the sound of a very fast car,
I like the sound of travelling far.

Liam Grandidge (13)
St Gabriel's RC High School, Bury

My Looney Toons

Bugs Bunny's my favourite loon,
He's grey and white, a cute furry sight,
In my opinion the best ever toon.
Taz spins round and round,
Making a funny whizzing sound.
Then there is Coyote,
He spends all day chasing Road Runner,
He will never catch her, she is too fast,
If he carries on the pursuit, he does not last.
Coyote will fall off a cliff with a great big thud,
His tricks and traps will never work,
Runner's too smart for the stupid jerk.
Marvin the Martian is small and smart,
But Sylvester and Tweety rule the part.
Porky Pig is short and fat,
Elmer the hunter wears a silly old hat.
They're weird and wacky just like me,
But they're all great and as cute as can be.

Laura Camps (12)
St Gabriel's RC High School, Bury

Friendships

A friend is someone to keep hold of,
To guide you through your fears,
They are always there,
They always care,
If you hurt yourself
You always have a friend,
Even if you don't know,
You will know if they like you,
Because they are always beside you.

Rachel Howarth (11)
St Gabriel's RC High School, Bury

TAKE A LITTLE TIME

Take a little time
To stop and look around
At all the things around you
Listen to the sound.

The darkness that I see
The sounds I never hear
Please don't pass me
And wish that I'm not here.

I don't want your pity
I don't want your tears
I just need a little
Of something that brings cheers.

Next time you see me
Waiting where or when
Just dip a little deeper
To put money in my tin.

Be grateful for what you have
Don't envy what you don't
Just think of me from time to time
A veteran of war.

Siobhan Shine (11)
St Gabriel's RC High School, Bury

THE WORLD

The world used to be a beautiful place,
Then it was ruined by the human race.

There were fields and meadows for miles around,
Now there's just tarmac on the ground.

Back then the air was clean and pure,
Now it's pollution and smoke galore.

We all need to help our world to go on,
If we don't it will soon be gone.

Katy Rector (12)
St Gabriel's RC High School, Bury

LENT

Lent is a time of joy and love,
When we remember our Lord above,
When we remember he died for us,
When we remember forgiveness and love.
Jesus was in the desert for 40 days,
It was a really big desert which seemed like a maze,
A devil came to him with temptation near,
But Jesus stayed loyal even though he had fears.
The devil tried to tempt him again and again,
The devil was evil, he hadn't been tamed.
So Jesus said no, he didn't give in,
Or he wouldn't be true, he wouldn't be livin'.
Jesus stayed loyal and so should we,
Not all people know him, not all people see,
So at the end of this poem we should think
We are *all* special, our Lord true,
The old *and* the new.

L   ovely
E   ggs and
N   ice
T   reats
    At Easter.

Kelsey Gafner (11)
St Gabriel's RC High School, Bury

MY HORRID LITTLE BROTHER

My brother's called Paul
Who I really can't stand.
He is so nasty
When his friends are around.

My sister is really cute,
But he picks on her.
I get into trouble,
It's just really not fair.

He is such a good boy
(At school that is)
But when he gets home,
He's so hard to miss.

My grandma said he's good,
In his dreams that is,
But we all know
What kind of boy he really is.

Louise Scranage (11)
St Gabriel's RC High School, Bury

NIGHT

Shadows creep across the moon,
black cats stalk by,
hear their cry
as it grows out of tune.

Bats screech in the dark,
wings flutter, dogs bark,
something lurks behind,
the silvery moon floats by.

Amber Wojciechowski (11)
St Gabriel's RC High School, Bury

THE SCHOOL BELL RANG

The school bell rang and the new ones ran in,
They were all excited, so was I,
First lesson was English, that was fun,
Maths was next, I had a big sigh.

The break bell rang and we all ran out,
I ran to my friends and we had a big laugh,
The loud boys made the teacher shout,
End of break and the whistle blew and everyone ran to the path.

We had our lessons and all the bells rang,
My friend and I caught the bus,
Then my other friend shouted, 'Bye.'

When I got back I told my cousins about
My day and how the school bells rang.

Elisabeth Osborne (11)
St Gabriel's RC High School, Bury

ON HALLOWE'EN NIGHT

On Hallowe'en night
The moon shone bright
The witches came out
And gave a shout!

With ghouls and ghosts
Walking headless hosts
It really is a spooky night
So don't go out, you'll get a fright
On Hallowe'en night.

Emma Gilligan (11)
St Gabriel's RC High School, Bury

THE SEASONS

The shoots are appearing small and green,
The air of spring is fresh and clean.
The sun is warm and the sky is blue,
In summer there are lots of fun things to do.
The leaves on the trees are turning brown,
The autumn rain makes me frown.
The falling snow makes everything white,
The sky is clear on a winter's night.
The seasons have colours, I've mentioned four,
I'm sure that you could think of many more.

Hannah Feehan (11)
St Gabriel's RC High School, Bury

SCHOOL

Early morning the alarm bell rings,
Eat my breakfast, gather my things,
Andrew calls and off we go,
Maths first thing, *oh no!*
The school bell rings, it's time to leave,
Off to the shop and then off home.

James Whittaker (11)
St Gabriel's RC High School, Bury

I SAW AN EARTHQUAKE IN THE SKY

I saw an earthquake in the sky,
I saw purple pigs flying by!
I saw a man as green as goo,
I saw a cat that looked just like you!
I saw a bird flying upside down,
I saw a dog wearing a crown!

I saw an elephant with flowers on its back,
I saw a mouse with wings painted black!
I saw a baby painted red,
I saw a cow with a pea-sized head!
I saw a lion that saw this too,
He roared at me and said they were strange but true!

Elizabeth Hayhoe (11)
St Gabriel's RC High School, Bury

COLOURS

Red is burning hot,
Green is growing grass,
White is a blank sheet of paper,
Purple is juicy grapes,
Pink is the sky at sunset,
Grey is as hard as steel.

Thomas Stebbings (11)
St Gabriel's RC High School, Bury

BREAK TIME

Everyone pushes out the door,
To play in the playground of fun galore.
The girls they just chat on the benches outside,
But the boys they have different things on their minds.
They jump on the field and they run all around,
They whoop and they yell and make a terrible sound.
The girls they sit down in their circle of friends,
They talk about music and all the latest trends.
The bell it soon rings, so we all go inside,
It's time for a curriculum learning ride.

Abigail Malley (11)
St Gabriel's RC High School, Bury

TERRORISM IN TWO DIFFERENT WORLDS

The frantic woman screamed,
Which made the young baby cry.
She couldn't help but break down in tears
As she watched her husband die.

The scared, young lady ran
Hoping she would survive,
But unfortunately three minutes later
She was no longer alive.

The planes bombed the citizens
Whilst 'looking' for the man,
Why didn't they understand?
He wasn't in Afghanistan?

The man looked at his best friend and said,
'I love my kids and wife,
But everything's changed now
Because when I jump I'll end my life.'

The terrified little girl looked around
At where her family's home once stood,
Crying into her mother's arms,
Which were soaked in her brother's blood.

'I love you too,' she gently whispered
But the phone had now gone dead,
As the watery tears crawled down her face
The widow shivered with dread.

The world leaders gathered together,
Negotiated and agreed what to do,
The wars, the violence would end completely,
But unfortunately this is the verse that's not true.

Katie Jamieson (13)
St Gabriel's RC High School, Bury

FANTASY LAND

Deep in the heart of the forest
Lived evil and terrifying beasts.
Though many now were at rest,
There were *some* awake at least.

The monstrous orcs ruled the land,
They fought many battles to do so.
The human castles crumbled like sand,
There was one land they did not rule, the elves said no.

The elves were ruled by Lord Tarmi,
He controlled a great power of magic.
The elves had an immense army,
That's why the orcs were so tragic.

But the orcs were greedy and strong,
And wanted to rule under the sun.
The elves were determined, and fought long,
Triumphantly, the *elves won!*

Jonathan Bradley (11)
St Gabriel's RC High School, Bury

ELEPHANTS IN THE ZOO

Elephants are so big and round,
They very rarely make a sound.
But when they run they sound like thunder,
You've got to move, no bloomin' wonder!

Stephanie Davies (11)
St Gabriel's RC High School, Bury

THE SCORPION

The scorpion's tail has an acid bite
It is trained to kill on sight

The scorpion is known as the 'desert stalker'
Using his claws he is a fast walker

The scorpion could survive a desert storm
As in a hole it hides its form

The scorpion's feared by many desert creatures
Its golden eyes, its stinger black, it shows its deadly features

The scorpion lacks size indeed, but certainly not pain
For many leave for desert trips never to be seen again

The scorpion. The scorpion he is a vicious fighter
And if you try to pick him up, you'll see that he's a biter

The scorpion. The scorpion. There's no one like the scorpion
For he's a fighter caped in black and he's killed a good few million.

Joe Sheedy (11)
St Peter's Catholic High School, Wigan

THE SOUNDS OF THE NIGHT

A dog howling in agony overpowered the wind's moans of anguish,
Until a chain of hollow howling became audible for all.
The winds sighed in a melancholy way,
No one answered its cry.

Suddenly, the wind and pain grew angry
And made the gnarled branches of the wizened trees
Smash each other against their will.
The peaceful trees, now corrupted.

Wolves determined to express their fury, cried angrily,
Competing against the wailing winds and the agonised dogs.
On the wolves bayed with all their dangerous might.

Night of woe, night of anger has forsaken this desolate moor,
Made solitary from the rest of the tranquil Earth.

Lorna Forrester (11)
St Peter's Catholic High School, Wigan

THE GAOL OF ST GEORGE

St George's flag is fluttering high.
The tower glares down, watching and waiting.
Pigeons are guards, follow every step.

The masses arrive, walking slowly.
There are numbers for lines where they must assemble -
Assemble in groups all over the yard.

Voices talk, scream and shout.
Wardens spy and yell commands.
Orders are issued, round and about.

Triangular rooftops offer no escape.
The air is rotten with the smell of pollution.
Cameras record every move down below.

As the victims are herded into the lair,
The Governor arrives and all is quiet.
Work begins to the sound of sighs.

In seven long hours, they'll all emerge
With happy smiles and cheerful eyes.

Rebecca Sharples (11)
St Wilfrid's CE High School, Blackburn

WAITING FOR THE END OF THE MATCH

Five minutes are left till the final whistle.
I'm waiting for the final score of the game.
It's raining, the rain sounding like pencils
dropping in bundles upon the floor.
22 players kick the ball around briskly.
There've been 85 minutes, about seven left.
I feel tense and nervous, like a grandma might.

I catch sight of a fan cheering insanely.
I feel scared. I think there's going to be a fight.
My team, in blue and white, look tired and ragged,
but still they run as if their lives depend on it.
The referee blows up and flies at a player.
I hope he's not seeing red, but I'm sure he is.

He turns his back and feels into his pocket.
The crowd scream and yell and wait for the colour.
I stay in my seat and see that it's yellow.

Matthew Clegg (12)
St Wilfrid's CE High School, Blackburn

AT THE END OF THE DAY

It's sunny and blue and a bit windy outside.
There are people in the room.
It's half past two and I'm waiting to come out of school.
In half an hour I'll be out of this lesson
Where I've stayed for so long and I'm feeling so hot.
I see people outside, talking in the distance.
I feel really happy starting my first year at school.

Gemma Edwards (11)
St Wilfrid's CE High School, Blackburn

MORNING DELIVERY

I'm waiting for the postman.
He's got my audition letter.
It's grey outside - a dull, lifeless world.
It's about seven o'clock.
I'm lonely and nervous.

There he is - the postman.
I'm excited now, though I don't know why.
He's in full uniform.
It's as though each new step's in slow motion.
He looks tired.
A door blocks my view.
Come on, I can't wait much longer.

The door closes. He starts walking again.
All I can hear is the *boom, boom* of my heart.
I see my letter being pulled out and run to the door.
Sorry, it says, and *not this time.*

Daniel Astley (12)
St Wilfrid's CE High School, Blackburn

GRAFFITI

John 9T8, says the spray on the big blue bin.
Matt woz ere is on the old brick wall.
Crisps lie crushed on the car park floor.
Tango bottles grow in the mossy grass,
With weeds in cracks growing green and flat.
Hello is scratched on paint on the sides of the walls.

Asid Bhatti (11)
St Wilfrid's CE High School, Blackburn

INSIDE

Old, dusty cobwebs are dotted round every cranny.
Patrolling pigeons perch peacefully in the tall, upright trees.
Razor wire waits eagerly to grab an intruder.
A patch of green and yellow dandelions hide in a dark brick wall.

Cars creep out of the large, black gates.
Large black fences throw their spikes round the building.
Tall red algae covers pillars standing to attention.
An old blue bin sits in a corner shouting, 'boo'.

Rusty silver gates prevent escape to the river.
The wind blows leaves along through the air,
Whistling to itself, quietly;
Floating along on a gentle, cold breeze.

Emma Woodruff (11)
St Wilfrid's CE High School, Blackburn

PRISON

A weather vane spins;
a clock sways in the wind.
The steeple on high watches us walk;
the pigeons, on guard, listen to us talk.
A hanging cross is firmly attached to the wall.
A bell screams loudly, ferocious and wild.

The sound of the bell makes me feel alone and lost inside.
The banging of doors vibrates in my head.
Then quiet.
I want to shout, but can't find my voice to yell.

Sophie Lowes (11)
St Wilfrid's CE High School, Blackburn

PRIZE-GIVING

I'm waiting for the swimming teacher to call Susannah,
waiting to collect my swimming cup.
It's dark outside and breezy too.
It's 8.30pm, two minutes to go.

The cup's picked up. I feel nervous and scared.
The man in green shorts and blue T-shirt
is wearing a smile, walking forward with pride.
A lady walks past him. He's no longer there.

Perhaps, I think, *he's dropped my cup.*
Perhaps, I think, *he's just vanished.*
But then I see the smile, still on his face.
I stand up and lean forward and hear a cheer.

Susannah Holden (12)
St Wilfrid's CE High School, Blackburn

THE UNKNOWN PARK

Yummy, yummy crisps are dotted on the floor.
Can you hear the squeak as I open the door?
A little yellow bug with its wings on its back
Sits on Santa Claus's special, red sack.
Voices of children holler as they run around.

There's a face on the wall that's not making a sound.
'Boo's' written boldly on a big black bin,
A big black bin that's made out of tin.
Cars zoom powerfully up the road,
Most will go home, carrying their load.

Laura Thurstan (11)
St Wilfrid's CE High School, Blackburn

WILL IT STAY OR WILL IT GO?

I'm waiting for an important decision -
waiting for my mum to say I can look after a cat,
waiting for my dad to say that I can't.
The weather's awful, the rain's beating the house.
I can see the cat shivering.
It's ten at night and I'm falling asleep.
I feel guilty I've caused so much argument.

I can see my mum coming.
I feel nervous and shake. I hope it's good news.
She's wearing her pj's, the checked ones,
looking happy - as if she's won.
She stops and bends down towards the floor.
Where's she gone?

Ahh, she's there, putting her slippers on.
But still I hear nothing. Silence.
My dad's now behind her, his face looking grim.
I think I'll stay quiet -
unless it's good news.

Jessica Rowe (12)
St Wilfrid's CE High School, Blackburn

PRIZE-WINNING

I'm waiting for Miss Claire, my dance teacher,
to say my name.
It's raining outside as hard as can be.
I can see lots of folk dancing - both young and old.
It's half-past nine, a whole hour to go.

I'm shaking now as I've never done before.
I see Miss Claire in a red shirt and grey pants.
She's walking as normal but looks excited.
A barmaid steps out and she disappears.

I panic, hear talking and shouting around me
And think the worst: that she's no longer there.
She appears from the crowd and I know
it's all over: I'll get my prize for my dancing this year.

Emily Rawsthorne (11)
St Wilfrid's CE High School, Blackburn

WAITING

I'm waiting for my mum.
I'm waiting to tell her about what I've just won.
It's raining outside.
I can see the clock, its hands ticking.
The time is three minutes and twelve seconds to six.
Three minutes and twelve seconds of precious time to wait.
I feel nervous, anxious and excited.

I can see the silver car in the distance,
sliding down the road.
I feel intense and sick.
My mum's wearing blue,
driving with concentration on her face.
She seems in another dimension, stressed.

She's gone out of sight - turned down a side road.
It's going to be a long wait.
But then she reappears outside our house.
I can hear horns beeping in the distance.
I can see the car drawing closer, pulling near.
I run down the stairs and throw open the door -
and wait for my mum to greet me.

Jennifer Haworth (11)
St Wilfrid's CE High School, Blackburn

TRAPPED

Every wall's plastered with graffiti -
white, chalky symbols that twist and flow.
Tall columns lean to one side -
and their bricks crumble to a dark claret dust.

There's a faint trickle of water.
A group of pigeons chatter, close by,
and loud shouts drift over from a gang of children
engaged in mock wars from another side.

Flooded drains burst with litter
and drinks cans crouch flat to the floor.
Alongside, torn crisp packets hop
to the beating breath of the wind.

On the front of the building a large white cross,
its skin peeling in the afternoon sun,
peers down at a congregation of rusting railings
standing still and straight in its shadow.

Callum Butler (11)
St Wilfrid's CE High School, Blackburn

WATCHING

A tower looms over the prison.
Pigeons walk back and forth, guarding.
Cameras hide in the darkness, watching.
Vehicles bring new convicts to this place . . .
Rails hold back the prisoners,
While razor wire protects the walls.
Prison guards watch all the time.

Joshua Leyland (12)
St Wilfrid's CE High School, Blackburn

THE LETTER

I'm waiting for the postman
to deliver a letter from BRGS.
It's drizzling outside and the wind is whining.
I can see the clock ticking - tick, tock, tick.
It's eleven o'clock, ten minutes to wait.

I see the faint red of a post van outside.
I'm nervous and shaking and aching inside.
The postman is wearing his little blue cap.
He's walking along slowly,
happy and whistling.
A car gets in the way where he's gone.

Now he's come back and I hear him whistling.
I see the letter in his hand.
I'm going to rip it open when I get it, I think.

Hannah Morton (11)
St Wilfrid's CE High School, Blackburn

DO NOT WAKE HIM

A hopping pigeon on the floor
tries to fly up to the sky.
White wings are all that I can see,
flying up in front of me.
The pigeon finally rests.
Quiet. Do not wake him yet.
Snoozing. Snoozing.
Shhhhhh.

Samantha Parker (11)
St Wilfrid's CE High School, Blackburn

MY BROTHER

I'm waiting for school to finish
to see my newborn baby brother.
It's raining outside and I hear a slight breeze.
People are running as I stare through the window.
It's three o'clock and there's fifteen minutes to go.

I catch sight of the clock when the door swings open.
I can imagine my brother in a sailor suit.
I run out of school, see my friend running for me.
She blocks out the view of my house on the hill,
and my baby brother who'll be there right now.

I run out of the gates and see birds in the air.
I follow them swiftly, keep moving and moving
to see my brother for the very first time.

Kayley Pickup (11)
St Wilfrid's CE High School, Blackburn

THE YARD

There's an old rusty bin with a scratched-off sticker,
and two black gates guard you whilst they shriek and shudder.

Cobwebbed gutters lurk high in the sky
and an isolated pigeon scavenges for bread on the ground.

A graffitied wall catches scraps of paper.
An old rusty trailer's hidden in the yard.

Barbed wire's on the rooftops and litter's everywhere.
The windows are rotten and weeds grow into the air.

I don't know what else there is - I haven't dared to look.
Keep your eyes to yourself and there'll be no bother.

James Fisher (12)
St Wilfrid's CE High School, Blackburn

FINAL SCORE

I'm waiting for the football match to come to an end,
Waiting to see if Burnley would win.
The sun is out and the fans are cheering.
It's 4pm, one minute to go.

Suddenly, there's a streaker running on the pitch,
Wearing nothing but a pair of socks.
He's obviously cold.
The mascot, a bee, blocks my view.

I see him again, his bottom's bare.
Everyone's laughing.
No one seems to care anymore
About what happens on the football pitch.

Adam Cumberlidge (12)
St Wilfrid's CE High School, Blackburn

WITH APOLOGIES TO CAROL-ANN DUFFY

I give you an acorn,
It is a small token of my love,
which will grow into a mighty oak of passion.

Like an acorn, our love grows,
and like an oak, it is yours until it dies,
The trunk is the ring of love, growing day by day.

The branches spread like our love,
and casts a shadow of our bond,
and the leaves growing to the light, cast by our pure love.

Jonathan Seward & Stephen Eccles (15)
Tottington High School

TERROR IN THE TOWERS

A normal Tuesday morning, a working day for all,
As the Twin Towers stood prominent and tall.
As the public turned their heads and looked towards Heaven,
Into the North Tower flew AA flight number 11.
As people screamed and commenced to flee,
The bad suddenly got worse at 9.03.
United Airlines flight 175 at 3 minutes past the hour
Penetrated the side of the famous South Tower.
Calls of desperation from victim to relative,
Unaware as to whether they would die or live.
Hundreds trapped inside, nothing they could do,
From victim to partner, the simple, 'I love you.'
Flames roared and plumes of smoke dispersed,
On the ground, wounded victims were nursed.
The attacks became the world's talk of the day
And at 10.03 am, the South Tower gave way.
As if it was peeled apart, the North Tower fell down,
Spreading debris and dust for miles around.
As to the ground below, the tower crashed,
Chances of finding survivors were severely dashed.
The emergency services came out in teams,
Searching and working against the screams.
As bodies were found, there were floods of tears,
Close relatives being forced to face their fears.
Searching for days and days became weeks
As debris was gradually cleared from the streets.
All families could do was pray and wait,
To learn of their poor kinsmen's fate.
Firemen scrutinised through masses of dirt and soot,
They never stopped, and hope never gave up.
Every single one labelled proudly as a hero,
For what was a horrifying day at Ground Zero.

The great heart of America, it still cries,
For the 3031 people who lost their lives.
The dust has settled and a scar has remained,
From the day the New York skyline changed.

Hannah Ingram (16)
Tottington High School

A LONG WAY FROM HOME

They are seeking asylum
They are seeking safety,
A new life, a new beginning,
No fear of persecution.

They travel empty-handed
They travel in fear,
A new country, with new hope,
Memories too painful to share.

They have energy and skills to contribute
They have protection against racial violence,
A new existence, education and work,
Restored pride and self-esteem.

They find no comfort
They find accusations,
A new name given with aggression from strangers,
Scroungers, beggars, crooks.

We are intolerant
We are suspicious,
A new form of maltreatment,
Discrimination is here, a long way from home.

Emily Sinkinson (15)
Tottington High School

IN MRS PARTRIDGE'S CLASS

Mrs Partridge dealing out the dreaded maths books
In the deadly dull classroom
Making tired children chant times tables
'One times one is one, two times one is two'

Horrific history, making me read out a whole page about Roman baths
Shocking science, learning about pathetic plants
Chaotic choir practice on Tuesdays
Singing sad songs over and over again

Weary Wednesday's half a week done
Forced to play recorder on Wednesdays
Helplessly hopeless at this though
Just watch other people and try to copy notes

Blissful break
Play time, praise the Lord, break from bawling of teacher
Playground packed with playful kids
Pelting balls the speed of light across the yard

Ring, ring, the bell goes
Back to boring lessons
Horrendous handwriting horribly hopeless at this
Having to write letters of alphabet again and again

Hooray, home time
There's no greater feeling
Until you remember where you are going tomorrow.

Jack Richardson (13)
Tottington High School

MUMS AND SONS

I don't want you to stay at home, son,
Because I don't think I could bear,
Taking you shopping for clothes, son,
When I know it's what you wouldn't wear!
Anyway, we'd have to walk, son,
And that's your worst nightmare!
And if you see the sweet shop, son,
I know you would only stand and stare!

You'd only get bored at home, son,
And then you'd start to complain,
And I don't want you watching TV, son,
Even though if you don't you'd be a pain!
When you're at school it's time for some peace, son,
Not hearing you play with our dog, Kane,
It's wrong to let you stay off school, son,
The teachers should have some of this pain!

I can't take you to the park instead, son,
As I can't afford the bus fare,
And you know we can't exactly walk, son,
Or it will be midnight before we get there!
So, off you go to school, son,
And I'm glad you've decided not to moan,
At last some peace and quiet without you, son,
Hmmm . . . but I don't really like it here alone!

Sarah Dixon (11)
Tottington High School

IN PRIMARY SCHOOL

Where are my stunning white socks?
My grey, prissy pinafore,
Who's taking me to school today?
Am I skipping, strolling or struggling to school?
Will I fall, bash, crash to the floor? Ouch!
Going through the village, valiantly.
Waving maniacally, madly at friends.

Now, in the deafening, destructive classroom, the clattering classroom
Bright, joyful clashing colours on the wall,
Lily asleep in the painted, perfected playhouse,
Squealing Stacey squawking, 'I want this, I want that',
Gossipy, gawping George, grassing on everyone to everyone.
Loopy Lucy swotting up, tying her tie, painting pictures,
Andrew Thomas pop, splash, his crisps bound to the floor,
Very simple Simon, conducting a wedding ceremony.

While in the dinner hall, the not so delightful food is served,
The undercooked, soggy, smelly excuse for meat,
The howl of the laughing hyenas from surrounding tables.
Squealing Stacey shouting, 'I want the cherry yoghurt,'
Playing hands in the middle,
Bossy Ben playing up to his role, head of the table
I'm just sat there wishing I could be him.

Home time now, I say my goodbyes,
But what will tomorrow bring?
Happiness? Sadness? A blue sky?
We walk past the lollipop man in his bright jacket, as bright as the sun.
We sometimes stop to talk to him; his face is always cheery,
Sometimes he will give you sweets if you are good,
As we struggle home, the sky becomes darker, winter's coming,
We rush home past the inviting toyshop to our warm, cosy,
                              comfortable house.

Jasmine Clarke (13)
Tottington High School

STUCK

I have to write a poem
'Choose any subject' the teacher said
'Perhaps something from the book we've just read'
But there are so many things going round in my head . . .
Where do I start?

I don't even like poetry
Most poems don't make any sense
Writing my own just makes me tense
Maybe it's me - I must be dense . . .
Where do I start?

I feel hopeless
Staring at these same four walls
Surrounded by screwed-up paper balls
It's agony - my brain stalls . . .
Where do I start?

I want to cry
My ticking clock is the only sound
Has it always been this loud?
Every silver lining has a cloud . . .
Where do I start?

I sigh
Everything I write is wrong
Poetry is an area where I am not strong
I've been thinking about this for way too long . . .
But how do I end?

Joelle Allen (16)
Tottington High School

A POEM BASED ON THE EVENTS OF SEPTEMBER 11TH, 2001

An immense, metallic bird soars into the tower,
People inside, without knowledge, without power,
Chaotic screams and cries, yet no one understands
As all heads are raised below, every woman, every man.

Expressionless faces on the streets below the scene,
The shock, the horror, resembling a bad dream,
As the dust envelops everything in its way
Innocent lives are abruptly taken away.

All at once the tower plummets to its death,
Bystanders watch, shed tears and lose their breath,
As the collapsing structure is converted into rubble,
Graves are produced for victims now out of trouble.

A year on from the disaster, sufferers can be left to lie,
What happened on that very day, no one knows a reason why,
The war is not yet over, our thoughts to the deceased
To those killed at Ground Zero, we leave you to rest in peace.

Rhianne Thompson (15)
Tottington High School

WHY?

Why?
Why do you look at me like that?
I ain't after your wallet, hey, I might just want a chat.
What do you think I'm going to do?
I's allowed to walk here too.
And why shouldn't I?
After all,
We all live under the same colour sky.

Don't matter what colour I am,
I mean, we all served together in Vietnam
Right?
Blacks and whites
Whites and blacks.
Reds and greens?
Sounds stupid when I put it like that.
It's just a colour
Simple as that.

Daniel Cartridge (16)
Tottington High School

MONDAY MORNING

Monday morning, Mrs Stroud's class, science first thing, what a blast.
Boiled water in a pan, my best mate Dan burns his hand.
Fifty seconds the gas on high, bubbles slowly rise and rise.
The thermometer rockets up and up until the liquid hits the top.
The school bell rings loud and proud, the teachers sigh to their relief
The kids are out from under their feet.
Children run all around, screaming, shouting out aloud,
Some girls sit upon the ground while other boys launch bricks around.

The classroom is damp and humid, and it is not very roomy,
Mrs Stroud scowls crossly at the smell of her black coffee.

Mrs Stroud speaks slightly Scottish,
Words she mumbles under her breath make us think we're in a mess.
Mrs Stroud is tall and thin, although she can make an awful din.

Last day of school at the disco, teachers make you dance and limbo.
Last dance of the school evening, ballroom dancing is not appealing.
The dance has finished, hip hip hooray, no more school for a holiday.

Tim Lever (15)
Tottington High School

SCHOOL

The brightly coloured room, the small things for small people.
Our first day, the alphabet spread across the walls, bells
ringing incessantly
Older kids kicking each other, new children crying as their
parents leave
New people, new places, new rules.

Everything bigger - our knowledge, our rooms, our attitudes, ourselves
We had own reading books, books with pictures, books with
information, books with hymns, books with our work
Rules more rigid, punishments profoundly understood.

End of the line, for a while at least, the last year of primary
The oldest, like gods, or shepherds over their sheep
SATs - passed and now prosperous
The making of wooden motor cars, lots of sports and messing around
was to come.

Back to square one - the small fish in the big pond again,
I didn't mind moving, moving on means growing up
Detentions, homework, buses, different rooms, different teachers
The bells still ring incessantly.

Michael Machell (13)
Tottington High School

SCHOOL TIME

Sitting at a battered desk,
Eyes keep straying out of the window,
Squeaking chalk sets teeth on edge,
As the hours pass so slow.

Poor old Miss at boiling point,
Shouting at the noisy rabble,
Pulling faces behind her back,
Lunchtime bell creates a scrabble.

Barging through the playground doors,
Excitement from every face,
Skipping ropes and muddy balls,
Boys and girls play kiss and chase.

Swapping biscuits, slurping juice,
Nibbled bread in grubby mitts,
Silly boys who taunt the girls,
Giggle loud at 'naughty bits'.

Sophie Jones (13)
Tottington High School

THE FIRE

Fiery fingers reach to the sky
Fire, fire, it never lies
Anything in its path the fire will burn
Causing humans much concern
Fire is so powerful and we cannot control it
Fire is also brilliant, we have always known it

Fire can end lives
As it thrives
In houses and in forests
No matter how many things it kills, fire is never sorry

Fire can be good
For some things such as burning wood
But it can also be a villain
Cause people much pain it can

Never underestimate the power of fire
If you do the consequences could be dire.

Joanne Cutt (11)
Tottington High School

IN MISS METCALF'S CLASS

Silver space cities made out of foil.
Weaving with wool bored me to death.
Break time monitor duty, answering
phones was so much fun,
Bulldog with the whole year.
Bright artwork on the wall and fancy
notice boards.
Assembly, the cold wooden floor,
Dancing boys dressed up like women.
'Freaky Fred shaved his head'
My teacher with her favourite orange coat.
And very oddly funny jokes.
We all performed a show, I danced, others sang.
We all signed shirts and had lots of fun.
At the end we all sang, 'Reach'
I enjoyed myself so much.
We were all going on together.
But most were all in tears.
The day ended with many cheers!

Sarah Waddington (13)
Tottington High School

THE JUNKYARD

Bits of metal sprawled along the floor,
Cars in piles, rusty and ruined,
Old trucks, fridges and beds,
Burnt up to a crisp,
Of course it must be the junkyard.

Sawn-up wood, bits of chairs, tables and old carpet,
Massing ever higher,
Papers trashed, bottles smashed,
Lying next to recycle bins,
Of course it must be the junkyard.

Rats crawling around the heaps,
Inhabiting the filthy, reeking mess,
Chewing wood and plastic bits,
Just looking at the sight can give you fits,
Of course it must be the junkyard.

Tramps and runaways scavenge the yard
Of all its worth, anything useful,
To try and make some money,
A completely hopeless cause,
Of course it must be the junkyard.

Paul Bradshaw (13)
Tottington High School

WITH APOLOGIES TO CAROL-ANN DUFFY

I give you this . . . match,
Like a flicker of passion,
This singular match,
From a box of many others,
Nothing makes it different,
Except for one thing alone.

That this single match,
Lit by us together,
Represents our love,
That lasts forever.

That one particular match,
Has the strength to survive,
The will to light a dark room
Just that one single match.

Us forever!

Storm Maguire (15) & Lorna Cole (14)
Tottington High School

ALL THINGS SHORT AND NASTY
(Sung to 'All Things Bright and Beautiful')

All things short and nasty,
All creatures short and squat.
All things mean and horrid,
The Lord God made the lot.

Each little pesky hornet,
Each fish and giant squid,
Who made the pesky vermin,
Who made the shark? He did.

All things short and nasty,
All creatures grey and grim.
All things plain and manky,
He made the bats, yes him.

Each little nasty wasp,
Each crocodile and hog,
Each slimy snake and spider,
Who made them all? Yes, God.

All things short and nasty,
All creatures short and squat.
All things mean and horrid,
The Lord God made the lot.

Mychael Barlow (14)
Tottington High School

FRIENDS

You should always look out for your friends,
As they will look out for you.
If you help them through troubled times,
They will help you.

If you spend a little time thinking about what you say to them
And don't open your mouth and say something to offend them,
They will always like and respect you,
As you did to them.

If you trust them and keep their secrets,
They will trust and do the same for you.
If you stick with them over time,
They will stick with you.

If you laugh when they laugh
And cry when they cry,
They will appreciate you
And do the same.

Of course we all know real friends are not like this,
It is just too good to be true.
But it's nice to think this way,
As long as they think with you for a change.

Denis Maxwell (14)
Witton Park High School

SCHOOL

School is depressing,
You can do lots of messing.

Friends are cool,
Teachers think they rule.

You can sit there talking
Whilst others are moaning.

Sometimes interesting,
Sometimes frustrating.

You can learn a lot
If you are smart.

If you sit fussing,
You will learn nothing.

Homework, homework, nothing better to do,
It stinks just like school.

Nafisa Mulla (13)
Witton Park High School

ENGLAND (MY POINT OF VIEW)

E   ngland is
N   ever boring,
G   reat place to live in,
L   ots of people live here,
A   lways raining,
N   ever sunny,
D   irty in places.

Gemma Redhead (14)
Witton Park High School

PARENTS SAY

The word that comes to my head when you say Mum
Is nag, nag, nag.

She has long, thin hair, small brain, but a big mouth
And already has eye bags.

She says . . .
'You're not going to stay young forever.'
Or,
'You're not that clever.'
And
'If you go out don't be late,
Otherwise I'll make you lick your dinner plate!'
And sometimes,
'You're not little miss perfect!'
And I say,
'Correct!'

Kulsoom Patel (13)
Witton Park High School

FRIENDS

F   riends are people whom you can trust,
R   eal friends are people you can share secrets with,
I   f you need help with something, they are always there,
E   very moment you spend with your friends will be one moment
     you'll never forget.
N   ever are you without support because you have friends,
D   on't ever shut friendship out of your life because one day you
     will need a friend.
S   pending time and making time for your friends is something
     which is important in friendship.

Zakeera Lorgat (13)
Witton Park High School

SCHOOL

School is boring,
School is sad,
It gets me moaning
and it makes me mad.
I've had enough,
I want to leave,
school is rough.
It makes me grieve,
most teachers bug,
they go on and on
sitting with their mugs,
I wish they were gone.
School is depressing,
It makes me want to cry,
the work keeps me guessing,
I'd love to say goodbye
but school means learning.
It can be fun,
I guess it's interesting,
except PE where we run.
Teachers can be alright,
they aren't always boring,
they just might
stop me moaning.
I guess it's not too bad,
I can live with it,
It doesn't make me too mad,
I'll just stick with it!

Raisha Mulla (14)
Witton Park High School

FRIENDS

Love is a word too hard to explain,
love is a word that brings you joy or pain,
but the love between us is of true friends
and this kind of love never ends.

Love in your heart wasn't put there to stay,
love isn't love unless you give it away,
look into my eyes, there you'll see
love is the friendship between you and me.

For every smile, every tear, for every burden,
every fear, whenever the road is too long.
Whenever the wind is too strong,
wherever this journey leads to,
I'll be there for you.

I wish for a sunbeam to warm you,
a moonbeam to charm you,
a sheltering angel so nothing can harm you,
laughter to cheer you,
faithful friends near you and every time you pray,
for God to hear you.

How long will we be friends?
Do you want clues?
As long as the stars twinkle in the sky,
as long as the angels are there up high,
till the water runs dry and until the day I
　　　Die!

Shama Shaikh (13)
Witton Park High School

MY MATES

Mates can be nice and friendly,
mates can be full of envy,
sometimes we shout
but it always works out,
I never know when they're about.

Sometimes we stay out late
and I know I'll always be her mate.
She even makes me feel good
when I am feeling full of hate.

Sometimes we fall out with one another
but we'll always be mates with each other.
We'll be friends for ever,
for ever and wherever.

Louise Carr (13)
Witton Park High School

FRIENDS

Friends are always there for you
In happy times and sad,
Helping and supporting you
Any time of day.

Laughter and sadness all in one
Caring and sharing, including everyone,
These are friends, everything you've got,
Without them nothing would be fun.

Parties, sleepovers, cinemas and parks,
Wherever you go, friends are never afar!

Roshan Patel (13)
Witton Park High School

FRIENDS TOGETHER

Friends will always stay with you,
Wherever you go,
In need of help, friends will be there.

Lost and on your own,
Got nobody with you,
Thinking of friends will make you feel comfortable.

Think of the fun you have together,
Making you feel as soft as a feather,
Friends cannot be taken away from you.

Having a friend is like being rich,
Having a whole lot of freedom,
Don't lose it.

Mahmood Patel (12)
Witton Park High School

WORTHLESS BOYFRIENDS

My best friend has a boyfriend
So now she has no time for me,
They do seem really happy -
Oh no - huge argument!
My friend is hysterical
So I have got to comfort her.

That boy over there is well fit!
Oh wow - he's coming over,
But he is just using me
So now I think that:
           All boys are worthless.

Kirsty Gudgeon (12)
Witton Park High School

I WISH I HAD A FRIEND

All alone I stand and stare
Waiting for the bus,
I'm getting cold and lonely,
How I wish I had a friend.

Everyone around me is
Sharing secrets with their friends,
I'm getting cold and lonely,
How I wish I had a friend.

Joking, laughing, having fun,
Everyone but me.
I'm getting cold and lonely,
How I wish I had a friend.

Someone's walking up to me,
'Hello, how are you?'
I'm not cold and lonely
Now I've got a friend.

Zoe Mercer (13)
Witton Park High School

COLOUR POETRY

Blue is the sound of birds singing in the tree,
Blue is the smell of a flower in the meadow,
Blue is the look of the sky above,
Blue is the taste of fresh mint,
Blue is the touch of the rain, cold and wet, beating on me,
Blue is the feeling of the wind blowing hard.

Cindy Eckersley (11)
Witton Park High School

WAR

As I lay in my bed,
the word *death* rises above my head.
Instead of being here right now,
I should be feeding my vicious hound.
Men are resting in their sleep,
but I must fight for world peace.
Broken bones and healing souls,
the flowers to remember the loved ones.
The dust and gloom,
in which men doom their death.
Day and night wars continue,
people's nerves shattered by death.

The foolish thought of saying war is great,
the men who say these aren't heroes of fate.
Despite dying for your country sounds great,
believe you me home is much greater.
War solves nothing,
apart from death.
The days are miserable, long and hard,
so stay at home to help yourself!

Mohammed Mulla (14)
Witton Park High School

FRIENDSHIP

Your friends are always there,
Through happiness and peace;
Through sorrow and grief;
You are never alone.

Aleasa Mobeen Awan (12)
Witton Park High School

GOOD MATES

We've been friends for ages,
from the age of 4,
We've never fallen out
and always knock on each other's door.

We've always been true friends,
like no other,
through all the difficult times,
and to keep each other out of bother.

We'll be friends for ever,
that's the way it should be,
always there for each other,
you and me.

Kari Littler (12)
Witton Park High School

RED

Red is the fine sweet scent of
Roses blooming in a field.
Red is the sound of the roaring fire
Crackling on a dark, cold night.
Red is the feel of soft delicate
Rose petals.
Red is the taste of strawberry ice cream
Melting away in your mouth.
Red is like the sun setting in the sky
On a hot summer's day.
Red is the comfort of the nice, warm fire glowing in the
Front room, on a cold winter's night.

Samantha Wilson (13)
Witton Park High School

SINKING

I thought there was something,
Something warm, something shared,
but now I think it's gone.

All that's left is an empty void,
One that's cold, one that's grey,
A cocoon,
To hide myself from you.

Why go far, far away,
When there is nothing, nothing wrong,
Nothing to stop a friendship
being shared.

If you stay you could
Have so much more,
Than if you go away.

Abigail Nottingham (13)
Witton Park High School

MY RED POEM

Red is the taste of a juicy red strawberry.
Red is the touch of a fluffy red pillow.
Red is the smell of sticky strawberry jam.

Red is the voice of a dressed up man,
Shouting and bawling at the top of his voice,
For the people to gather to join his clan.

Red is the sight of my cousin's bedroom.
Red makes me feel sad and blue.
Red makes me feel a moaner and a loner.

Leigh Lennon (11)
Witton Park High School

BEST FRIENDS!

We're best friends,
True as can be,
We never fall out,
Not you or me.

We're there for each other,
Through the bad times and the good,
We help each other out,
Like best friends should.

I've known you for a long time,
Since the age of four,
And I hope to know you,
For a long time more.

Rebecca Hocking (12)
Witton Park High School

MY MATES

I had a good mate called Fred,
We said we'd be mates till we're dead,
But one day we fell out,
Boy, we didn't half shout,
But I've made a new friend instead.

My new mate is called Danny Jones,
Unlike Fred, *he* never moans,
He's a bit of a swot,
But I like him a lot,
And our friendship's as strong as hard stones.

Luke Allen (12)
Witton Park High Schoo

FRIENDSHIP!

A good true friend is rare and unique,
they will be there for you through thick and thin,
you know you can trust them no matter where
they would help you until you win.
A friendship between the best of two people
is strong and unbreakable,
it isn't always found anywhere
but you know the friendship is unmistakable.
You'll be friends forver with a friendship so strong.
No matter what anyone does
nothing can go wrong.
What could hurt you so much more
is if this friendship was no more.
You would never talk to one another,
turn away and off you would go.

Hanna Mulla (12)
Witton Park High School

MY BEST FRIEND

My best friend is a computer mad freak,
He also hates to eat boiled leek,
He is a friend whose head's bigger than him,
So we call him big-head, but he prefers the name, Tim.
My friend thinks he can earn money,
Just from being really funny,
But his jokes are as bad as his breath,
But they are overdone by his yellow teeth,
They are so yellow they can take over the sun.
After all this, my friend is an alright guy, but
He can be really fun.

Matthew Bradshaw (12)
Witton Park High School

ESCAPE FROM REALITY

The only place I can go to get away from things,
The only place I can go to think deep thoughts,
The only place to miss when you're away,
The only place that feels truly yours.

The only place that's warm and comfortable,
The only place you keep your possessions,
The only place where you can share your thoughts,
The only place full of personal memories.

The only place where you can hide away,
The only place you can dream and hope,
The only place you can stay all day inside of,
The only place to sit back and wonder.

The only place you can't bear to leave,
The only place you want to spend each moment,
The only place to sleep and dream,
The only place to escape from reality.

Shivdatta Gonsai (14)
Witton Park High School

A GOOD FRIENDSHIP, A BAD FRIENDSHIP

A friendship is like a rock,
very hard to break.
A friendship is like a concrete wall,
you need something tough to knock it down.

A friendship is like a sour sweet,
when you chew it gets very sour.
A friendship is like a sharp knife,
when your back is turned it can wound.

David Crutchley (12)
Witton Park High School

THERE ONCE WAS A KING

There was once a king,
Who was fair and true,
His sword *slayer* was mighty.
Easily splitting boulders asunder
And cutting swathes of foes.
His armour made of pure gold,
His shield of his dragon,
His horse was noble
And could gallop faster than another could run.
He had sworn to protect the weak
And gains glory,
Without death as his minion
And his crown, made of his finest jewels,
Now rests us upon his chest,
Never to be worn again.

Michael Tillotson (14)
Witton Park High School

A GOOD FRIENDSHIP

Friendship, friendship, it's all about the best,
Take good care of your big nest.

A friend is someone who you can trust,
Not a person who's all about lust.
He will take your pride and always give in,
One day he'll come and shove you in the bin.

A friend would be there when you are ill,
And would comfort you when you are blue.

A friend is like being rich,
He will be your life of freedom.

Zakir Bhamji (12)
Witton Park High School

REDRUM THE CLOWN

His name is Redrum the clown,
He wears no smile but an evil frown,
His eyes aren't cheerful or inviting but evil and frightening,
His laugh isn't playful but scary,
His hands are clammy and hairy,
His hair isn't frizzy or colourful but long, dark and dreadful,
His act isn't entertaining but horror itself,
He has a small, bold assistant who resembles an elf,
Neither of them makes a good act, they're really rubbish in fact
He doesn't ride a trike but a big, fiery motorbike,
He came straight from Hell to make us scream and yell,
He walks around just grunting,
He'll wait under your bed until morning,
He'll come into your dreams and give you nightmares,
He's not like the clowns you see at fairs,
He loves pain and rebels against hope,
He hates religious icons such as the Pope,
He says he's old and foolish to have belief and that
Eventually we'll all end up beneath,
So if you see Redrum the clown, pack your bags and get out of town,
Don't look back, stop or trip at all, because
Redrum the clown will catch you before you fall.

Bradley Pickering (14)
Witton Park High School

BLUE

Blue is like a warm, peaceful sea,
It is like a clear, cloudless sky,
It is the colour that most people wear,
It is like cool water running down your throat.

Maddiha Mahmood (11)
Witton Park High School

THE BELL

The bell rings, rings, rings
It brings, brings, brings children to the classes
Morning registration is so boring
Tutor says how appalling
I think I'm in for a fright
The teacher says you'll be alright
The bell rang, *ding, ding*
I got outside and all I saw
Were pupils who looked very mean.
I entered the class
And the bell rang, *ding, ding*
Lesson began, I ran
The bell rang, *ding, ding*
Lunchtime now, it's munch time
The bell rang, *ding, ding*
Children start rushing
With a bit of pushing
Two lessons go by like a fly
And home time
The bell rang, *ding, ding.*

Sakib Zarif (15)
Witton Park High School

BLUE

Blue is like sadness on a cold, rainy day
Blue is the sky far, far away
Blue is the sea with fish all around it
Blue is my favourite colour,
It's always soft and gentle.

Naomi Halsall (12)
Witton Park High School

BEAUTY OF THE WORLD

Have you ever noticed the beauty of this world
And the contents of this beauty which surrounds us all?
From the largest of the creatures; to the very small,
From the sun and from the moon, from every rise and fall.
But . . .
Every little act of nature is different,
Every little fact is different.
Every drop of rain that you've ever seen fall,
Every flake of snow is different,
Every place you go is different,
Everyone you know is different,
That's the beauty of it all.

Ismail Chothia (14)
Witton Park High School

CELEBRATION

C   hristmas is a day of celebration,
E   id is the time for Muslims,
L   ove is the day of Valentine's,
E   veryone should learn to celebrate,
B   right days bring good fun,
R   owing causes hatred,
A   nger and ferociousness causes fights,
T   alking calmly causes happiness,
I   llnesses are often caused by stress,
O   n happy occasions
N   o one should mess!

Samira Patel (13)
Witton Park High School

LILAC

Lilac is like a pansy swaying in the breeze
Lilac is my bedroom and curtains
Which lets me look at the trees
Lilac is my second favourite ice cream
Lilac is my favourite gel pen
Lilac is my happy colour
Lilac is my favourite colour.

L ovely
I love lilac
L uscious
A mazing
C razy.

Carla Meikleham (11)
Witton Park High School

MY DEVOTION TO MOTORCYCLES

M ad about motorcycles,
O ffering support towards racers,
T he joy of winning 1st place in a race,
O vertaking all the rest,
R iding the best,
C ollecting the trophy,
Y does it hurt when you fall off?
C leaning,
L eading the pack,
E nding the race in one piece.

Steven Anderton (15)
Witton Park High School

DEATH IN BELIEF

I think with no belief at all,
just waiting for the wonders of mystery
to come from upon the darkness of death.

The light shines on an open part of the mind,
releasing memories of past told stories.

It happens without fact
explaining the purpose of this flashback.
Then a cold hand appears,
putting pressure on a limb.

This face seen before asks, why?
Then reality is brought back,
the face disappears,
the eternal light of life stops.

The arms are open
and it's over,
the door closes,
then love blossoms to me.

Andrew Hogg (14)
Witton Park High School

FOOTBALL

Football is the world's greatest sport,
It is known around the world.
You can hear the crowd cheer,
Whilst they go for a beer.

You've got the best,
You've got the worst,
In the olden days we had Geoff Hurst.

Manchester United are the team today,
But will they go all the way?
They have Becks and also Giggs,
They both like to show of their tricks.

Bobby Whittingham (14)
Witton Park High School

IT'S NO HEROIN(E)

Anything is good enough for them
Just one packet will do
A sniff, a tablet or an injection
As long as it makes them feel
On top of the world.
With the constant hallucinations
They think they know it all
All starry-eyed
With no concept of reality
Ecstatic and content.

But how long will it last?
A couple of hours of paradise is it?
It's all a scam!
Want to dance all night?
Still want to see tomorrow?
Well there's no guarantee.
Brain damage
And other bodily harm
That's guaranteed!

Yasmeen Patel (15)
Witton Park High School

LOVE

Your love is like a candle,
burning bright,
an eternal flame,
that will never die.

Take my heart,
so I have none,
but you'll keep me alive,
through this eternal bond.

Our hearts are one,
they'll never break,
keep me close,
for our sake.

You'll be in my mind,
always and forever,
no matter where we are,
we'll always be together.

Krishna Kaur (15)
Witton Park High School

THE MIRROR

The mirror stands lonely,
Lonely and bare,
You walk past it and stand and glare.
The mirror reflects light,
Light which helps you to see,
The mirror is important,
Well . . . it is to me.

Ashley Littler (13)
Witton Park High School

THE OWL

The owl is a predator,
That hunts in the night,
Graceful it soars through the night sky.

As the owl sleeps,
We bustle and hustle around,
Then as we sleep,
The owl hunts down its prey,
With precision and grace.

As the owl hunts down a mouse,
We are asleep within a house,
The owl's excellent vision shows it the way,
Through the night sky, blue, black and grey.

The sun has come up,
The owl lays down to rest,
The start of our new day
And the owl is asleep waiting for dark.

Daniel Chadwick (14)
Witton Park High School

ONE MAN'S LIFE

The ridges of a man's shoes are another beast's mountains,
The eyelashes of a man's eye is another beast's grassland,
The saliva of one man's tongue is yet another beast's sea,
One man's weapon is another beast's tool,
One man's friendship is another beast's anguish,
One man's hate is another beast's love.

One man's life is another beast's death.

Andrew Hall (14)
Witton Park High School

TIME

Alarm goes off in the mornin',
School again, how borin',
Before you know it, you're in your first lesson,
Cryin' your heart out, full of depression.

Another exam, time and time again,
The bell will ring, just don't know when.
I look outside and see the great, wet sky,
It's usually every hour, I snap and lie.

Finally my seven hour day is over,
I come home and get attacked by Rover.
Will I ever get any peace,
Or shall I eat all day and become obese?

The weekdays fly by,
Saturday's here, time for a rough ride.
I enter a house of music,
Suddenly I'm flat out, my face covered in lipstick.

3am, knock, knock, knock on the door,
Mum opens, what a *roar!*
Thrown out of the house,
Meet a new friend, call him Mr Mouse.

Early mornin', appears the sun,
Has my life just begun?
How fast time flies, today's already over, friends I met,
First there was sunrise, now there's sunset.

Adam Mirza (16)
Witton Park High School

SOMEONE SPECIAL

They brighten the morning, like a hot summer's day,
The love you feel for them never goes away.
The joy of seeing them fills your heart,
The way in which a candle lights the dark.

Cold tears fall like rivers,
As nightmares draw nearer to becoming reality.
The day I wake up and everything's as before,
The day, for the rest of my life I'll long for.

How will the rivers cried ever dry away?
How will the love return and mistakes be forgotten?
Will I ever be forgiven,
Or will the loneliness become my new best friend?

Days seem like weeks, weeks like years,
Memories begin to wash away, but the heartache lives on.
You know I'd do anything for you,
Please forgive me.

The pain felt for what seemed like years, has now gone,
The scent of friendship has returned,
I'd never put myself through the torment again,
Because the next time I'll just remember that . . .

Friends brighten the morning, like a hot summer's day,
The love you feel for them never goes away.
The joy of seeing them fills your heart,
The way in which a candle lights the dark.

Yasmeen Bhamji (14)
Witton Park High School

FRIENDSHIP

Friendship is where you share
Or where you care
Where you do things together
Whatever the weather
Be together all day and all night
There's no fright
When there's a fight they will stop and stare
But they don't care if they're not there
In the same school
In the same class
Live next door
But it doesn't matter as long as you're there
That's what friendship is about
To care and to share
To look after each other and be there
For one another
They'll do each other's hair
And have a laugh but who cares
As long as you're there
And have friends too.

Lyndsey Battrick (13)
Witton Park High School

BROKEN

The stars twinkling bright
Just the way you used to look at me,
The wind brushes my face,
Softly, slowly,
Just the way you used to touch my face.
The sun's rays vibrant and bright
Just the way you were
Now things have changed.

The sand slowly picks itself up
Drifts away, treading slowly
Just the way you suddenly left.
The water trickles away,
Bending round the stones and broken bricks.
Just the way I feel now,
I am broken.

Rehana Khansia (15)
Witton Park High School

THE RUNNING MAN

He is running, running as fast as he can,
Trying not to look back.
He is running for his life,
What to do, where to turn, he doesn't know.
He is heading for the fence, can he make it?
A sound, a cry of a mockingbird,
A second sound, it was a gun.
He's been shot but still he is on the run.
The guards are chasing him with batons,
His innocence makes him faster.
He runs like the wind, he is nearly there.
The fence is getting closer and closer.
He is there. Suddenly, several shots are heard,
A mockingbird falls to the ground.
He's been shot, fallen he's gone down,
He is laying there in his own pool.
His black, velvet skin becomes red and wet.
There is no life in him,
Except the jerking of his leg.

Nargis Chand (15)
Witton Park High School

WHAT DOES IT LOOK LIKE?

Is it ugly, beautiful
Or just a pretty . . . ?

Is it dangerous and frightening,
Or just kind and nice?

Is it little and shuffles,
Or big and struggles?

Is it quick and wicked,
Or slow and lazy?

Is it soft and safe,
Or does hard = harm?

Is it something you cannot imagine,
Or just the *word?*

Amit Chudasama (15)
Witton Park High School

CHOCOLATE

It can be light brown,
Dark brown or white.
It comes in packets,
Or a hot drink at night.
Chunky, crunchy or smooth,
Whatever the texture,
Whatever the mood.
Either an ice cream or in bars,
Milky Way, Galaxy, Snickers or Mars.

Clare Stokes (15)
Witton Park High School

NANA

Her name is precious it will never grow old,
It's engraved in my heart in letters of gold.

When I need her she's always near,
This is why I hold her so dear.

She was right there beside my mum and my dad,
Both when times were good and when they were bad.

Even when she's gone and has passed away,
Memories of her smiles will always stay.

When I need comfort she'll always be there,
She cuddles me tightly to show that she cares.

She is so gentle and pure like a dove
This is why it's my nana I love.

Her name is precious it will never grow old,
It's engraved in my heart in letters of gold.

Lisa Chadwick (15)
Witton Park High School

LOVE

Love is blind
Love is kind
I love you
Please don't mind
Some love one
Some love two
I love one
And that is you.

Sharlene Smalley (15)
Witton Park High School

THE WAR POEM

Today is the day I go to war
To kill people and nothing more
I am terrified
What will I do?
What will I see?
This will be a sight to see.

I am here in the trench
It's dark and cold
And the walls are full of mould
My friends and I all know
We are going to die
Over the top we go
And all the soldiers
Are dropping like flies.

The mud is in my boots
All these men in suits
Are running our way
Oh I wish I was home
Back in my day.

Lisa Jolley (15)
Witton Park High School

BLACK

Black is beautiful like the eclipse,
black is the exquisite smell of the night sky,
black is the screeching sound of nightfall,
black is the soft touch of a rabbit.
Black is the sweet taste of blackberries melting
in your mouth.

Alex Jackson (11)
Witton Park High School

THE PAIN AND THE FEAR

War, war we'll have no more,
The pain, the fear and the bore.
The shells, the guns and even the gas,
But soon this time will eventually pass.

Time, time well it had gone by,
The many times that I would cry.
I could hear the boy in the dugout next door,
The pain, the fear and much, much more.

This is the day I'm proud to be here,
I'm going over the top and yet I have no fear.
With soldiers by my side and a gun in my hand,
Hopefully I'll return back from *no-man's-land.*

I served my country,
I served my family,
I served the soldiers that were around me.
Yet I only served myself with pain and fear
And the thoughts that will be around for many years.

My duty is now done, the pain and fear is now over,
I'll let God take me back to my home in Dover.

Gemma Whalley (15)
Witton Park High School

COLOUR POEM

Blue is like the sky of summer
it is like the blueberries, bursting in your mouth
it is like the puff of wind on a hot summer's day
it is like the icy cold day. on a cold winter's day
you can feel the fresh fragrance of winter.

Hafeez Mohammed (14)
Witton Park High School

ENCOUNTER

A single smile
Filled with excitement and joy.
An overwhelming vision
A few spare words
And scattered thoughts.
Sense of emotion and
Sense of loss.
An eternal wound.

Farhana Badat (16)
Witton Park High School

CREATIVITY

The paper is white,
Boring in front of me.
There is nothing happening,
No creativity.
Creativity is in the stars,
Stars twinkle like the moon,
Peaceful and calm.

Kelly Clegg & Ashley Littler (15)
Witton Park High School

GREEN

Green is like the emerald cat-like eyes
It is like the smell of the grapes on a tall green vine
It is like the wind blowing on the grass beneath your feet
It is like the leaves that change colour in autumn
It is like the tangiest unripened pear
It is like the bittersweet taste of happiness.

Saima Bi (13)
Witton Park High School

GOLD!

Gold is like the sun on a hot scorching day,
Gold smells like you're going to win the lottery,
Gold is like a rare, golden eagle, swooping to catch its prey,
Gold feels like you're on cloud nine on a warm summer's day,
Gold tastes like enjoyment when something good is about to happen,
Gold is happiness when you find a solid gold bar and
Going to the shop and donating it to charity.

Nathan Hadfield (13)
Witton Park High School

BLUE

Blue is the colour of our eyes,
Blue is the colour of the sky,
Blue is the colour of the water which we swim in.
Blue is the taste of delicious blueberry ice cream,
Which slurps down us,
Blue is the colour we adore
Blue is the colour that we look at
When we look into our eyes or at the sky.

Emma Jeal (13)
Witton Park High School

BLUE

Blue is like the deep blue sea
Blue is like the smell of fresh ocean air
Blue is like the sound of waves crashing against the rocks
Blue is like the touch of clear, fresh water
Blue is like the taste of blueberries freshly picked from a bush
Blue is the feeling of a cold winter's night.

Shane Cockerill (13)
Witton Park High School

FOUR SEASONS

Autumn,
Leaves on the ground, brown, red and yellow,
Crunching beneath my feet,
Bare trees standing still.

Winter,
Soft snow, white as milk,
An icy wind blowing in my face.

Spring,
Emerald-green grass swaying in the breeze, thin and long.
Birds singing their peaceful song.

Summer,
The blazing sun shining down,
Heating up the ground.

Shamima Sidat (15)
Witton Park High School

RED

Red feels like blood
Red feels like a dead heart
Red tastes like outdated tomatoes
Red sees the day of judgement
The sound of red is spooky
The sight is scary
And it tastes like *hot, hot*
Cold chilli.

Iftikhar Patel (10)
Witton Park High School

WAITING!

I've been here, at the beach, for over an hour,
The weather is really nice and warm.
I feel burning hot.
The warm, sweaty sun is reflecting on my body and hair.
I can hear the seagulls in the air,
Squawking like children in a playground.
I might have to wait for 10-15 minutes now.
I shout, 'Where are you?'
I finally spot her,
I feel very relieved,
My heart starts beating again.
I can hear the sea bashing a rock against a wall like a ball.
The light, breezy wind makes it very hard to breathe
As I get nearer,
But she's here now!

Zahira Hanif (13)
Witton Park High School

BLUE

Blue is like a puddle on the pavement
Blue is the colour of the beautiful sky
It is like the calm endless sea
It is like the taste of fresh, cool water
Blue feels like cold, damp ice
It is like the happiness of young children
It is like the blue whale
Swimming peacefully in the sea.

Farrah Desai (11)
Witton Park High School

A WAR POEM

It's cold, it's musty, the trenches are all dusty,
It's glum not fun, we are lacking rum,
I feel like crying or even worse, dying,
These friends of mine are on the front line,
By tomorrow I hope they're still fine.

Another day has dawned but it is still the same,
Nothing to gain, just a little more pain.
Will I die, will I not? Today is the day I go over the top.
All I can hear is shells flying by, oh how I wish I could die.
I am horrified now I want to go home, I have a family of my own.
I can hear the noises getting closer, I can see the lights brighter.
I see a gun shot coming by as I clench my fist and start to die.

Louis Grant (14)
Witton Park High School

BLACK POETRY

Black is burning in the sky
Like the pupil of my eye
All that's black is evil and sad
It's everyone's anger, all that's mad
Black gives me shivers down my spine
It makes us so sad, we start to whine
Black is the colour of witchs' blood
A world without black would be happy and good.

Samuel Cain (11)
Witton Park High School

FRIENDSHIP

Friends are people who help each other, when they need help.
Friends are people who lend things to each other.
Friends are people that get on all the time.
Friends are people who buy each other things when they have no
money.
Friends are people that don't lie to each other.
Friends are people that take care of you when you are ill.
Friends are people who make you happy when you are sad.
Friends are people that don't fight with you.
Friends are people that make you laugh nearly all the time.

Danielle Tomlinson (13)
Witton Park High School

THERE IS NOTHING YOU CAN'T DO

Never judge a book by its cover
We are all the same deep inside
Never be afraid to speak
Or your questions may never be answered
You should express your feelings
Don't hide them behind a wall
Try not to be someone who you're not
Be yourself and be the best you can be
Give everything good a try
There is nothing you can't do.

Francesca Docherty (13)
Witton Park High School

BLUE

Blue is like the sound of the sea,
It is like the smell of blueberries.
Blue is like the taste of soft, chewy bubblegum,
It feels like the comfy uniform you are wearing.
Blue is a calm and relaxing colour,
Blue is my favourite colour.

*B*ig	*B*eautiful
*L*umpy	*L*aughing
*U*gly	*U*nusual
*E*ggs	*E*lves

Blue is the best!

Nosheen Akhtar (11)
Witton Park High School

YELLOW

Yellow is like the sun that shines away all day.
Yellow is like the smell of a crowd of daffodils,
beside the lake, dancing in the breeze.
Yellow is like the soft crackling of the fireplace,
on a winter's night.
Yellow is like the honey that can be as sweet as candy.
Yellow is the colour of the moon,
glowing on a summer's night.

Sobia Rahman (13)
Witton Park High School

BLUE

Blue is like the soft cushion that I keep on my chair,
It's like the bluebell that grows all year round.
Blue is like the heart of the fresh, blue trickling water.
Blue feels like the air, that flows through the sky above
And down below, that's because it flows through my hair.
Blue water is the sea, that all sea creatures live in.
Blue is my colour that keeps me warm, morning and night.
Blue is the colour that makes me float in the sky,
So very high.
All of this is not a lie,
It's a porky pie.

Karl Taylor (13)
Witton Park High School

COLOUR POEM

Purple is the feeling of happiness,
of children playing in the park.

Purple is the taste of autumn berries,
picked from trees.

Purple is what you see in your family's
life of love and friendship.

And purple is the sunset of the night,
as the day has faded by.

Toby Ainsworth (13)
Witton Park High School

RED

Red is the bloodless hound feeding on its prey.
Red is the smell of violence, filling the air.
Red is the monster, crying out its pain.
Red is the touch of a dart piercing my heart.
Red is the taste of blood, coming out of my nose.
Red is the rash, spreading over me, whole.
Red is the boy who took away my heart.
Red is the emotions of hate and fright.
Red is love, which took away my soul.
Red is the killer who was covered in blood.
Red is a sign that shows it will be your time.

Irham Javed (13)
Witton Park High School

BLUE IS . . .

Blue is a blueberry growing on a tree
Blue is a stream of water trickling down a mountain
A splodge of ink on a page.

Blue is a sea with calm, gentle waves
Blue is a flower with beautiful petals
The colour of my own eyes.

Blue is a colour that is freezing cold
Blue is the colour of a raindrop
Blue is my favourite colour.

Brendan Webster (11)
Witton Park High School

YOU'VE HEARD OF LENNOX

As a heavyweight champ we know him.

Lennox Lewis the boxer supreme,
To be as famous one day, for many,
Would be their ultimate dream.

He was born in London in 1965
Once dreamed of being a fireman
But is one of the most famed boxers alive.

His mum, she was called Violet
He never knew his dad
He wasn't very bothered
It didn't make him sad.

He was not a good student
He got expelled from school
He did not understand
The main school rules.

Lennox is a sporting hero
He fights clean and always wins
He is the Heavyweight Champion of the World
Can anyone knock him off his pins?

After 12 rounds of boxing
The judge had to decide
Who to give the fight to
To Lennox because he had an easy ride.

So if you see him in the arena
In a strip of red and white
Don't shout out loser
You may get in a fight.

Adnaan Iqbal (13)
Witton Park High School

MY DREAMS

The moon shines so brightly
In the sky at night
And as I sleep upon my bed
My dreams all take flight.

Last night I dreamed,
I was a pirate upon a ship,
With treasure all around me,
And it was the captain of the ship,
Then I was a footballer,
Scoring all the goals,
Then I was a fireman,
Saving people's souls,
After that I was in
A massive submarine
500 feet under the sea
And as I continue with my dream
The moon still shone on me.

As I dreamed the night away
My thoughts blasted into space
I was an astronaut
Standing on the moon.
The moon that has a face
That smiles so brightly
In the sky at night.

Mark Willacy (12)
Witton Park High School